Images & Imagination

Ernst Peter Fischer

Faszination Forschung

La fascination de la recherche

Captivating science

Ciencia fascinante

Images &

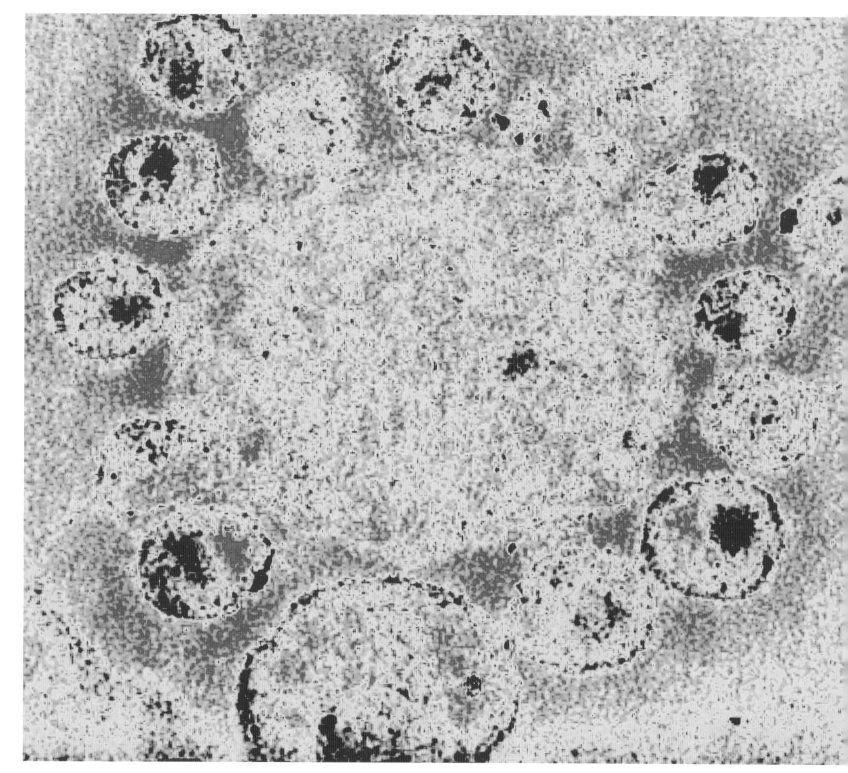

Imagination

Inhalt

Table des matières

Contents

Índice

Einsichten

Albert Einstein hat einmal gesagt: «Das Schönste, was wir erleben können, ist das Geheimnisvolle. Es ist das Grundgefühl, das an der Wiege von wahrer Kunst und Wissenschaft steht.» Er brachte damit zum Ausdruck, dass Wissenschaft mehr ist als der Versuch, das noch Unbekannte zu entdecken und das noch Ungelöste zu lösen. Beim Blick in den Mikrokosmos des Lebens entdeckt man das Geheimnisvolle ebenso wie die Schönheit. Wissenschaftler, die täglich damit befasst sind, dem Geheimnis der Lebensvorgänge auf die Spur zu kommen, halten ihre Erkenntnisse in Bildern fest. Dabei entstehen Momentaufnahmen des Mikrokosmos, die nicht nur die Wissenschaftler selbst, sondern ein viel breiteres Publikum ansprechen, da sie oft von außerordentlichem ästhetischem Reiz sind. Sie gefallen uns, und daher können wir sie zu Recht als Kunstwerke der besonderen Art einordnen. Denn Natur ist schön, wenn sie aussieht wie Kunst, und Kunst ist schön, wenn sie aussieht wie Natur. So steht es bei Immanuel Kant, dem Philosophen der Aufklärung, und angesichts des vorliegenden Bildbandes fällt es sicher nicht schwer, ihm zuzustimmen.

Viele der hier gezeigten Bilder aus der Roche-Forschung gleichen kleinen Kunstwerken. Auch wenn sie im Grunde lediglich dem medizinischen Erkenntnisgewinn dienen, können wir nach ihrem ästhetischen Reiz fragen. Wir sind eingeladen, darüber nachzudenken, warum diese Bilder und damit die Forschung, der sie entstammen, eine so große Faszination auf uns ausüben.

Wir wünschen allen Betrachtern umfassende Einsichten durch die mikroskopischen Ansichten, die wir in diesem Buch zusammengetragen haben. Sie lassen die besondere Qualität unserer Forschung erkennen, die wir sonst als «state of the art» bezeichnen. Ein Ausdruck, der in diesem Buch eine neue Bedeutung erhält.

Intérieurs

Einstein a dit qu'il n'y avait rien de plus beau que le mystérieux, qu'il n'y avait, sans mystère, ni art ni science véritables. On ne saurait mieux dire que le propos de la science n'est pas seulement de découvrir ce que l'homme ignore encore ou de résoudre ce qui est encore en attente de solution. Lorsque le regard pénètre le microcosme de la vie, on s'aperçoit que le mystérieux y voisine avec le beau. Les scientifiques qui, chaque jour, traquent le mystère de la vie fixent leurs découvertes sous forme d'images. D'une beauté souvent extraordinaire, ces instantanés captent aussi bien l'imagination des profanes que celle des scientifiques. Ils nous plaisent et nous pouvons voir en eux des œuvres d'art d'un genre particulier. Car la nature est belle quand elle ressemble à l'art, comme l'art est beau lorsqu'il ressemble à la nature. C'est ce que disait Kant, philosophe des Lumières. Comment ne pas en convenir avec lui en contemplant les clichés de ce volume?

Les images que nous avons réunies ici proviennent de la recherche Roche. Bien qu'ayant, au fond, pour seul but l'accroissement des connaissances médicales, beaucoup d'entre elles apparaissent comme de véritables œuvres d'art. Comment ne pas s'interroger, dès lors, sur ce qui fait leur séduction esthétique et sur la fascination qu'à travers elles exerce sur nous la recherche?

Nous espérons que le lecteur aura du plaisir à feuilleter ce livre. Les vues microscopiques qu'il présente témoignent de la qualité de la recherche Roche. Une recherche dont nous disons, d'une expression qui prend dans ce livre un sens nouveau, qu'elle s'effectue «dans les règles de l'art».

Insights

Intro-visión

Albert Einstein once said, 'The most beautiful thing we can experience is the mysterious. It is the source of all true art and science'. This statement expresses the view that science is more than just a striving to know the unknown and to solve the unsolved. A gaze into the microcosmos of life reveals both mystery and beauty. Scientists who spend their working lives unravelling the mysteries of biological processes capture their findings in the form of images. The resulting snapshots of the microcosmos are attractive not just to the scientists themselves, but also to a wider public, as they are often of extraordinary aesthetic charm. Since we find them appealing, we can legitimately regard them as works of art. For according to Immanuel Kant, the 18th century philosopher, nature is beautiful if it looks like art, and art is beautiful if it looks like nature – a sentiment anyone who sees this collection of images is likely to share.

Many of the images from Roche research shown here are, in effect, small works of art. Though their only explicit purpose is to advance medical knowledge, we are entitled to consider their aesthetic appeal and to ask why we find them, and hence the research that underlies them, so fascinating.

We hope that the microscope images collected in this book will provide a broad range of insights to all who see them. They show the particular quality of our research that we refer to as 'state of the art' – an expression that takes on new meaning in this book.

Albert Einstein dijo en cierta ocasión: «La cosa más hermosa que podemos experimentar es el misterio. Es la fuente de todo verdadero arte y de toda verdadera ciencia.» Esta frase expresa claramente que la ciencia es algo más que el intento de descubrir lo que aún permanece oculto y dar respuesta a lo que aún carece de ella. Si uno contempla el microcosmos de la vida, verá en él misterio y belleza. Los científicos, empeñados a diario en desentrañar el secreto de los procesos biológicos, fijan sus descubrimientos en forma de imágenes. De una belleza estética a menudo extraordinaria, las instantáneas así obtenidas son elocuentes no sólo para los propios científicos, sino también para el resto de las personas. Nos agradan, y por lo tanto podemos clasificarlas con toda razón como obras de arte de un tipo especial. Pues la naturaleza es hermosa cuando imita al arte, y el arte es hermoso cuando imita a la naturaleza. Así opinaba Kant, el filósofo de la Ilustración, y a buen seguro no nos resultará difícil darle la razón tras hojear el presente libro.

Muchas de las imágenes recogidas en esta obra, procedentes de la investigación de Roche, son pequeñas obras de arte cuyo único objetivo era la obtención de conocimientos médicos. Podemos, no obstante, preguntarnos por su atractivo estético y el motivo de la fascinación que tanto ellas como la propia investigación ejercen sobre todos nosotros.

Confío en que las imágenes microscópicas reunidas en este libro sirvan para introducir al lector observador a una amplia visión de la ciencia. Son prueba de la gran calidad de la investigación en Roche, que los científicos gustan de llamar a la inglesa «state of the art» (literalmente, «estado del arte»), con una expresión que en este libro adquiere un nuevo sentido.

Jonathan Knowles
Head of Global Pharmaceutical Research at Roche

Zentrales Nervensystem

Welten im Kopf

Le système nerveux central

Des mondes dans la tête

The central nervous system

The world inside our heads

Sistema nervioso central

Un universo en la cabeza

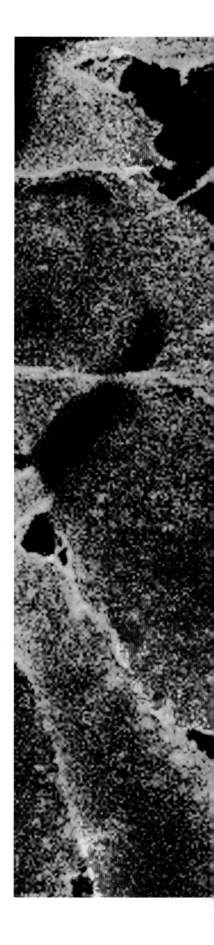

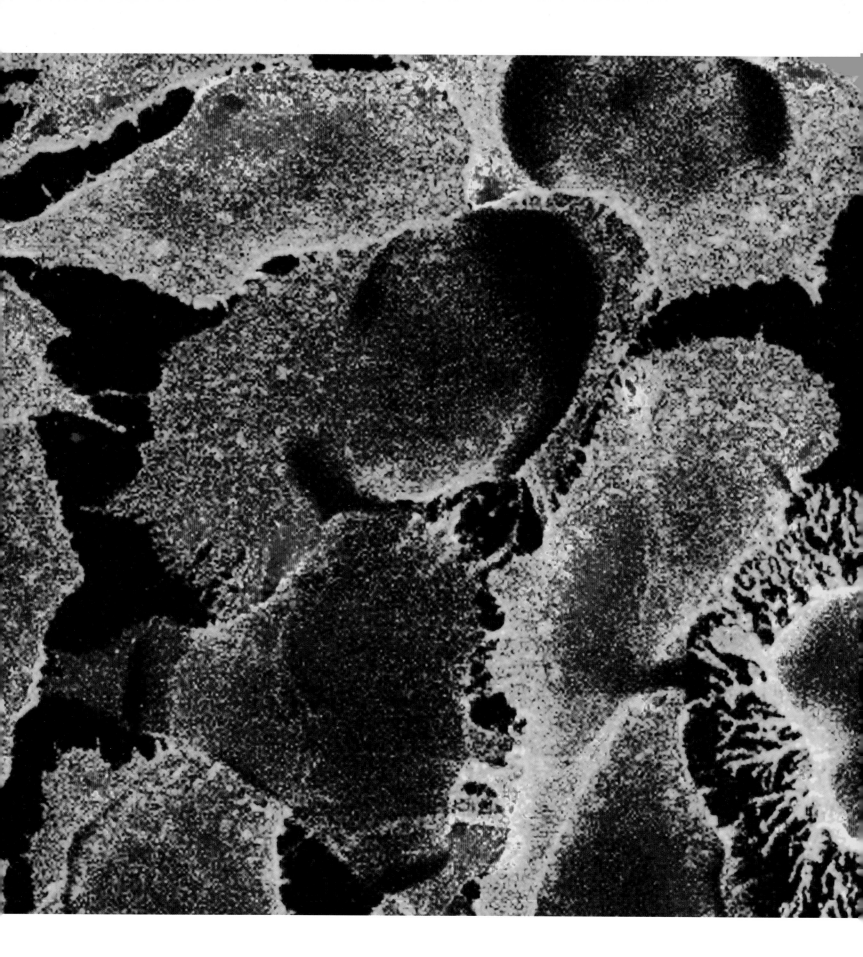

Welten im Kopf

Des mondes dans la tête

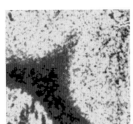

Als die Wissenschaft vor rund 400 Jahren ihre moderne und bis heute wohl organisierte Form bekam, hatten sich ihre Begründer vor allem vorgenommen, damit die Lebensbedingungen der Menschen zu verbessern. Wissenschaft sollte nützlich sein, und es ist keine Frage, dass dies hervorragend gelungen ist. Im Laufe der Zeit ist sie aber nicht nur immer präziser, sie ist zugleich auch ansprechender geworden und bringt mit ihren stets verfeinerten Methoden immer reizvollere Bilder und Ansichten der Natur hervor. Spätestens seit Beginn des 20. Jahrhunderts haben aufmerksame Beobachter der fortschreitenden Wissenschaft festgestellt, dass dieses große geistige Abenteuer der Menschheit nicht nur unsere täglichen Bedürfnisse befriedigt, sondern auch unseren ästhetischen Sinn anspricht.

Zwischen dem Gefallen am Schönen und der Anwendung des Nützlichen liegt das Gewinnen von Erkenntnissen. Lange Zeit wurde die Frage, was wissenschaftliches Verständnis charakterisiert, mit Hinweisen auf eine Art innere Logik der Forschung beantwortet. Auf den Entwurf einer Hypothese folgt das Experiment, also die Frage an die Natur, um sie zu prüfen. Doch diese Sichtweise erklärt nicht, was die Forscher selbst an den Bildern der Wissenschaft so fasziniert. Die Aufnahmen und Darstellungen werden aufgrund neuer Techniken immer raffinierter gestaltet und ästhetisch anspruchsvoller präsentiert, auch wenn dies nicht bewusst geschieht und der wissenschaftliche Erkenntnisgewinn immer im Vordergrund steht. Doch Wissenschaft wird von Menschen gemacht, und Menschen erfreuen sich an Schönheit. Am Anfang unseres Bilderbogens aus der Welt der Wissenschaft steht das zentrale Nervensystem, das unter anderem zwischen dem Auge und dem Bewusstsein vermittelt und somit die Voraussetzung für die Wahrnehmung der Abbildungen ist. Auf diese Weise generieren wir Bilder in unserem Kopf, an denen sich unsere Imagination entzündet.

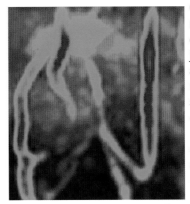

Quand la science prit, il y a environ 400 ans, la forme moderne et organisée qu'elle a conservée jusqu'à nos jours, ses fondateurs avaient surtout pour projet d'améliorer la vie des hommes. La science devait être utile, ce en quoi elle a brillamment réussi. Non seulement elle est devenue sans cesse plus précise, mais aussi toujours plus belle à regarder. En s'affinant, ses méthodes nous donnent de la nature des images de plus en plus belles. Des observateurs attentifs avaient noté dès le début du XXème siècle, sinon avant, que cette grande aventure de l'esprit n'était pas qu'utilitaire et qu'elle flattait aussi notre goût du beau.

Entre le plaisir esthétique et la préoccupation utilitaire, il y a la quête scientifique. Mais pourquoi les chercheurs cherchent-ils? En réponse à cette question, on a longtemps invoqué une logique de la recherche poussant les scientifiques à formuler des hypothèses qu'ils vérifient ensuite expérimentalement, en questionnant la nature. Cela n'explique cependant pas qu'ils soient eux-mêmes fascinés par les images que leur révèle la science. Des images qui, le progrès technique aidant, sont présentées de manière toujours plus raffinée, toujours plus esthétique, pas toujours consciemment d'ailleurs, puisque l'obtention des connaissances prime toute autre considération. C'est que derrière la science il y a l'homme, et l'homme aime le beau. Nous avons réuni à votre intention, sur les pages qui suivent, un certain nombre de ces images du monde de la science qui parlent à l'imagination. En commençant par le système nerveux central, qui conditionne, par sa fonction de médiateur entre l'œil et la conscience, la perception des images que nous générons et dont a besoin notre imagination.

PP. 8/9: Immunolabelled neuronal cells. Confocal fluorescence microscopy, Remo Hochstrasser, Roche Basel.

The world inside our heads

Un universo en la cabeza

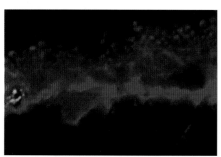

Around 400 years ago, when science assumed the modern and well organised form that it retains today, its founders considered its primary function to be that of improving the living conditions of human beings. Science was meant to be useful, and it has undoubtedly succeeded most wonderfully in this respect. Over this period it has become not just more and more precise, but also, thanks to increasingly sophisticated techniques, more appealing in terms of the ever more attractive images and views of nature that it provides. By the turn of the 20th century it had become apparent to attentive observers of the progress of science that this great intellectual adventure of mankind not only satisfies our material needs but also appeals to our aesthetic sense.

Somewhere between the appreciation of beauty and the practical application of scientific findings lies the acquisition of knowledge. The question of what characterises scientific understanding has long been answered by reference to a research method in which hypotheses are put forward and then tested in experiments, that is, by reference to nature. This view, however, cannot explain why researchers are so fascinated by scientific images. Thanks to new techniques, these have become increasingly refined in form and aesthetically ambitious in presentation, though not by intention, since their primary role is that of tools in the acquisition of scientific knowledge. Nevertheless, science is made by human beings, and human beings take pleasure in beauty. On the following pages we present images from the world of science that excite the imagination. We start with the central nervous system, which mediates between our eyes and our consciousness and is thus essential for perception of the images that we generate and require as food for our imagination.

Cuando la ciencia adquirió, hará unos 400 años, su forma moderna y la organización que aún hoy conserva, sus fundadores se propusieron sobre todo mejorar gracias a ella las condiciones de vida del ser humano. La ciencia había de ser útil, y no cabe duda de que ello se ha cumplido de forma admirable. Durante este tiempo, la ciencia no sólo se ha hecho más y más precisa, sino al mismo tiempo también más atractiva. Sus métodos perfeccionados sin cesar nos ofrecen imágenes de la naturaleza cada vez más hermosas. A comienzos del siglo XX, si no antes, los observadores atentos de los avances científicos comprobaron que esta gran aventura intelectual de la humanidad no sólo puede satisfacer nuestras necesidades materiales, sino también nuestro sentido estético.

Entre el placer de lo hermoso y la utilidad de lo aplicable queda la búsqueda de conocimientos. A la cuestión de qué caracteriza al conocimiento científico hace tiempo que se ha respondido con referencia a una lógica de la investigación que lleva a los científicos a plantear hipótesis para verificarlas a continuación experimentalmente, lo cual no es otra cosa que una pregunta a la naturaleza. Pero este planteamiento no explica qué hay en las imágenes científicas que tanto fascina a los investigadores. Las nuevas técnicas permiten obtener imágenes cada vez más complejas y más bellas, aunque sea de forma involuntaria, puesto que la obtención de conocimientos científicos se halla en la base de tales avances tecnológicos. Pero la ciencia la hacen personas, y las personas aman la belleza. En las páginas siguientes encontraremos diversos ejemplos de imágenes científicas que estimulan nuestra imaginación. Y comenzaremos nuestro recorrido por el sistema nervioso central, intermediario entre el ojo y la consciencia, y requisito imprescindible, pues, para la percepción de las imágenes que generamos y precisamos para nuestra imaginación.

Zentrales Nervensystem
Le système nerveux central
The central nervous system
Sistema nervioso central

An bestimmten Orten im Gehirn befinden sich Moleküle (Rezeptoren), die als therapeutische Angriffspunkte dienen können. Bei der Suche nach solchen Orten entstand dieses dynamische Bild. Die sichtbar werdende Form setzt unsere Gestaltwahrnehmung in Gang, und wir beginnen, nach den erkennbaren Symmetrien und ihren Brechungen zu suchen. Wissenschaftlich relevant sind die gelblich-roten Wölbungen und Windungen, die dem Forscher die gesuchten Angriffspunkte zeigen.

Cette image très dynamique a été obtenue en cherchant dans le cerveau d'un rat des molécules auxquelles puissent se lier des médicaments, autrement dit des récepteurs faisant office de cibles thérapeutiques. Les contours qui se matérialisent sous nos yeux mettent en route notre sens de la perception des formes, nous poussant aussitôt à chercher des symétries et des ruptures de symétrie. Le scientifique, lui, va s'intéresser aux arrondis de l'image, c'est-à-dire aux parties en jaune et en rouge, car c'est là que se trouvent les récepteurs qu'il désire étudier.

This visually dynamic image took shape during a search for sites in the brain where large receptor molecules that can serve as targets for drugs are located. As it becomes visible, the image activates our perception of shape, and we start to look for identifiable symmetries and asymmetries. Of scientific relevance are the yellowish-red curves and convolutions that indicate to the scientist the location of potential sites of attack by drugs.

Esta imagen dinámica se obtuvo durante la búsqueda de la localización cerebral de receptores que puedan servir como dianas terapéuticas. La imagen que comienza a formarse activa nuestro sistema de percepción de las formas, y comenzamos a buscar simetrías y asimetrías identificables. Desde el punto de vista científico tienen interés las curvas y sinuosidades rojo-amarillentas, que indican a los investigadores la localización de los receptores buscados.

Distribution of ionotropic glutamate receptors in a horizontal section of a rat brain revealed by receptor radioautography. Pseudocolour computer image, Grayson Richards, Roche Basel.

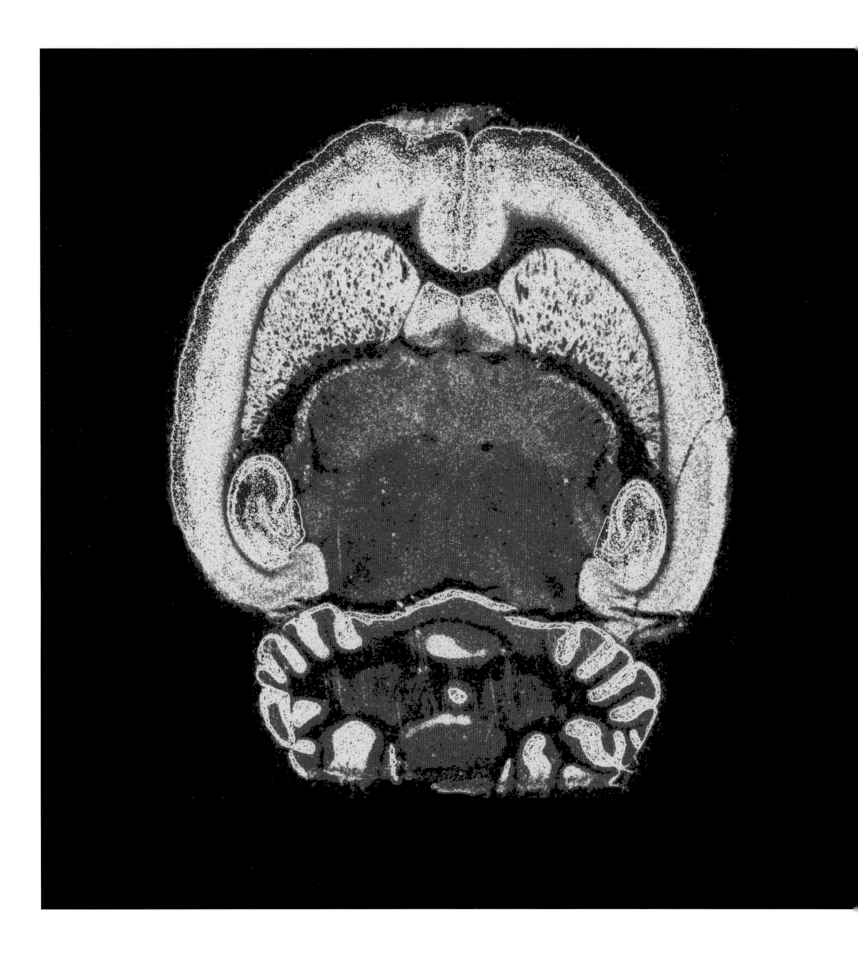

Zentrales Nervensystem
Le système nerveux central
The central nervous system
Sistema nervioso central

Eine verwirrende Doppelung: Auf diesem Bild sehen wir eine Netzhaut, und wir sehen sie mit unserer Netzhaut. Der mikroskopische Schnitt durch eine Retina wurde mit Hilfe von Antikörpern gefärbt, die an zwei unterschiedlichen Zielen binden. Die Mikrofotografie ist Teil der Experimente, die sich um ein genaues Verständnis des Sehvorgangs bemühen. In dieser und ähnlichen Aufnahmen kommt es zu einem faszinierenden Wechselspiel der beiden komplementären Farben Rot und Grün, das durch gelbe Strukturen ergänzt wird.

Nous voyons cette image avec notre rétine et, en même temps, nous voyons sur cette image une rétine. La coloration de la coupe microscopique de cette rétine est obtenue grâce à des anticorps qui vont se lier à deux cibles différentes. Cette microphotographie fait partie des expériences grâce auxquelles on s'efforce de mieux comprendre le phénomène de la vision. La complémentarité du rouge et du vert compose, en alternant les deux couleurs, un ensemble fascinant, que complètent des structures colorées en jaune.

We look at this image with our retina, and at the same time we are looking at a retina in the image. Shown here is a microscopic section through a retina. Staining is achieved by means of antibodies that direct themselves toward and bind to two targets. This photomicrograph was produced in the course of experiments aimed at elucidating the precise mechanism of eyesight. In this and other images there is a fascinating interplay between the complementary colours red and green and a further contrast with yellow structures.

Vemos esta imagen con nuestra retina, y al mismo tiempo vemos en esta imagen una retina. Se trata, más concretamente, de un corte microscópico de la retina de una rata teñido con ayuda de dos anticuerpos específicos. Esta microfotografía forma parte de una serie de experimentos tendentes a esclarecer los mecanismos íntimos de la visión. Destaca la fascinante alternancia de los dos colores complementarios rojo y verde, intercalados con otras estructuras de color amarillo.

Section through a rat retina. Confocal fluorescence microscopy, Heinz Wässle, Max Planck Institute for Brain Research, Frankfurt am Main.

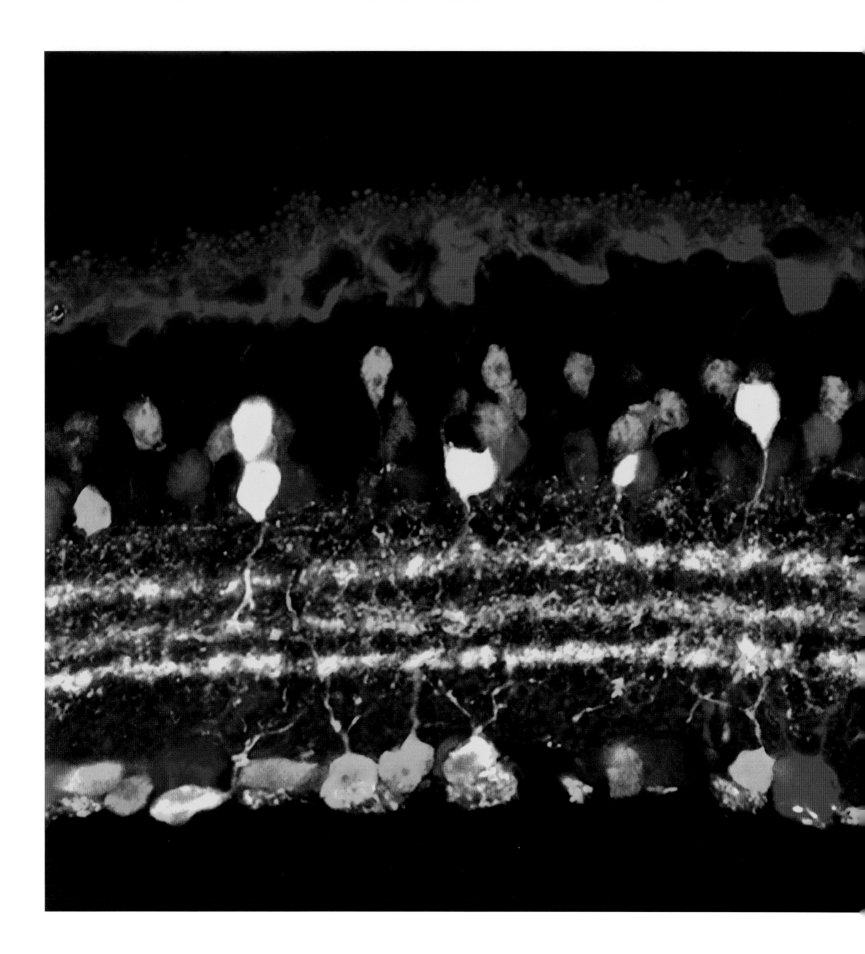

Zentrales Nervensystem
Le système nerveux central
The central nervous system
Sistema nervioso central

Die technischen Methoden, mit deren Hilfe man heute in das Innenleben von Zellen blicken kann, werden immer raffinierter. So ist es heute möglich, Zellen mit mikroskopisch gesteuerten Laserpulsen auf Oberflächen zu bringen, die eine Durchleuchtung der Zellen zulassen. Das dazugehörige Instrument wird als «Laser Capture Microscope» bezeichnet. So kann das quirlige Innenleben der Neuronen bewundert und auf seine biochemischen Bestandteile hin analysiert werden. Der ästhetische Reiz entsteht durch den Kontrast der glatten Außenwelt und der feinverästelten Innenwelt, aber auch dadurch, dass kein Ende des Strömens zu erkennen ist.

Les techniques permettant au regard de pénétrer à l'intérieur même des cellules s'affinent pour ainsi dire de jour en jour. Exemple, cette méthode grâce à laquelle les pulsions d'un rayon laser dirigé sous contrôle microscopique permettent d'amener des cellules sur des surfaces particulièrement perméables à la lumière. On peut admirer sur cette image le fourmillement intense de la vie intérieure des neurones et analyser les éléments biochimiques dont elle se compose. Le charme de ce cliché ne naît pas que du contraste entre un monde extérieur parfaitement lisse et un monde intérieur grouillant de vie, il est aussi dû au fait que rien ne semble jamais devoir mettre fin à ce flux.

The technical methods used to look inside cells are becoming ever more sophisticated. For example, microscope-guided laser pulses can be used to attach cells to suitable surfaces for imaging. The instrument concerned is known as a laser capture microscope. In this image, the bustling inner life of neurons can be admired and at the same time analysed in terms of its biochemical constituents. The aesthetic appeal is derived not only from the contrast between the smooth outer world and the restless inner world, but also from the apparent endlessness of the flow within the neurons.

Las técnicas utilizadas para visualizar el interior de las células son cada vez más perfectas. Hoy es ya posible, mediante pulsos microscópicos de láser, disponer las células sobre las superficies más adecuadas para su transiluminación. Ese instrumento, denominado «microscopio de captura de láser», nos permite admirar la bulliciosa vida interior de las neuronas y analizar los elementos bioquímicos que las integran. El atractivo estético de esta imagen es atribuible no sólo al contraste entre la uniformidad del mundo exterior y el heterogéneo ajetreo interior, sino también al hecho de que el flujo intracelular no parece tener fin.

Neurons from the dentate gyrus of the hippocampus extracted from a section of mouse brain. Laser capture microscopy, Nila Mehta, Maria Geraci, Susan Wojcik, Roche Nutley.

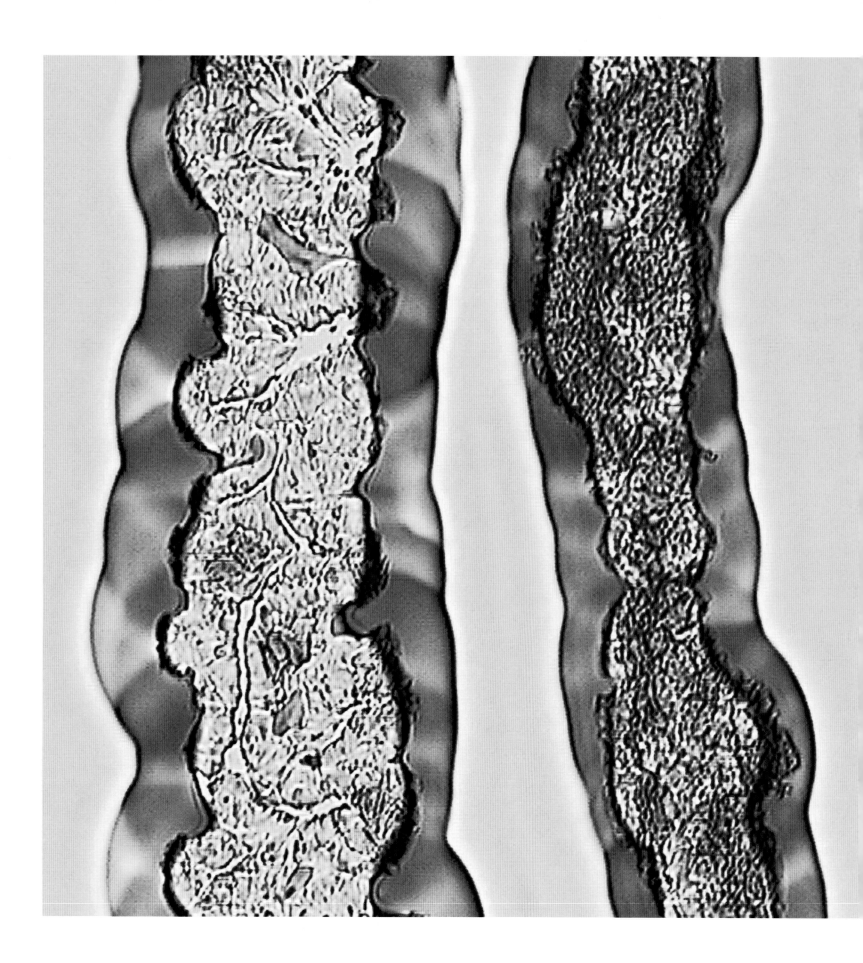

Zentrales Nervensystem
Le système nerveux central
The central nervous system
Sistema nervioso central

Neuronale Zellkultur mit Immunmarkierung eines Antigens – so lautet die exakte Bezeichnung des gezeigten Bildes, und es lässt sich wohl kaum deutlicher veranschaulichen, wie wenig oft die wissenschaftliche Information mit dem unmittelbaren Eindruck zu tun hat, den solch ein Bild hinterlässt. Die sachliche Auskunft wird keineswegs dem gerecht, was dem Auge geboten wird und den Betrachter in Spannung hält. Sofort stellt sich das Gefühl des Geheimnisvollen, der mysteriösen Schönheit ein. Man meint, in ein Dickicht, in einen Zelldschungel zu blicken, und weiß zugleich, dass man die Grundlagen des eigenen Lebens betrachtet.

Culture de cellules nerveuses avec marquage immunologique d'un antigène, proclame l'intitulé scientifique de ce cliché. On ne saurait mieux faire toucher du doigt tout ce qui peut séparer une information scientifique de ce que l'on est susceptible de ressentir en regardant une image telle que celle-ci. D'un côté, quelques termes techniques dans toute leur sécheresse. De l'autre, une impression de mystère et de beauté. L'impression de plonger au cœur d'un taillis, d'une jungle de cellules, en sachant que l'on a sous les yeux les fondements de sa propre vie.

The title 'Neuronal cell culture with immunolabelled antigen' could scarcely have been better chosen to highlight the gulf between the scientific information about this image and the subjective impression that the image creates. In no way does the factual information do justice to the riveting effect of the image on the eye of the viewer. There is an immediate and pervasive feeling of mysterious beauty. We seem to be looking into a thicket, a cell jungle, yet at the same time we are aware that what we are seeing is the basis of our own life.

Citocultivo neuronal con inmunomarcaje antigénico; tal es el título exacto de esta imagen, y resulta difícil destacar de forma más gráfica la disparidad entre la descripción científica objetiva y la impresión subjetiva que esta imagen suscita en el observador. La fría información técnica no hace en modo alguno justicia al cautivador efecto visual que ejerce la imagen. Ésta despierta en el observador una sensación de misterio y belleza, como si uno vislumbrara el interior de un matorral, de una selva celular, y al mismo tiempo fuera consciente de estar contemplando los fundamentos de la propia vida.

Neuronal cell culture (cytoskeleton) with immunolabelled antigen. Fluorescence microscopy, Remo Hochstrasser, Roche Basel.

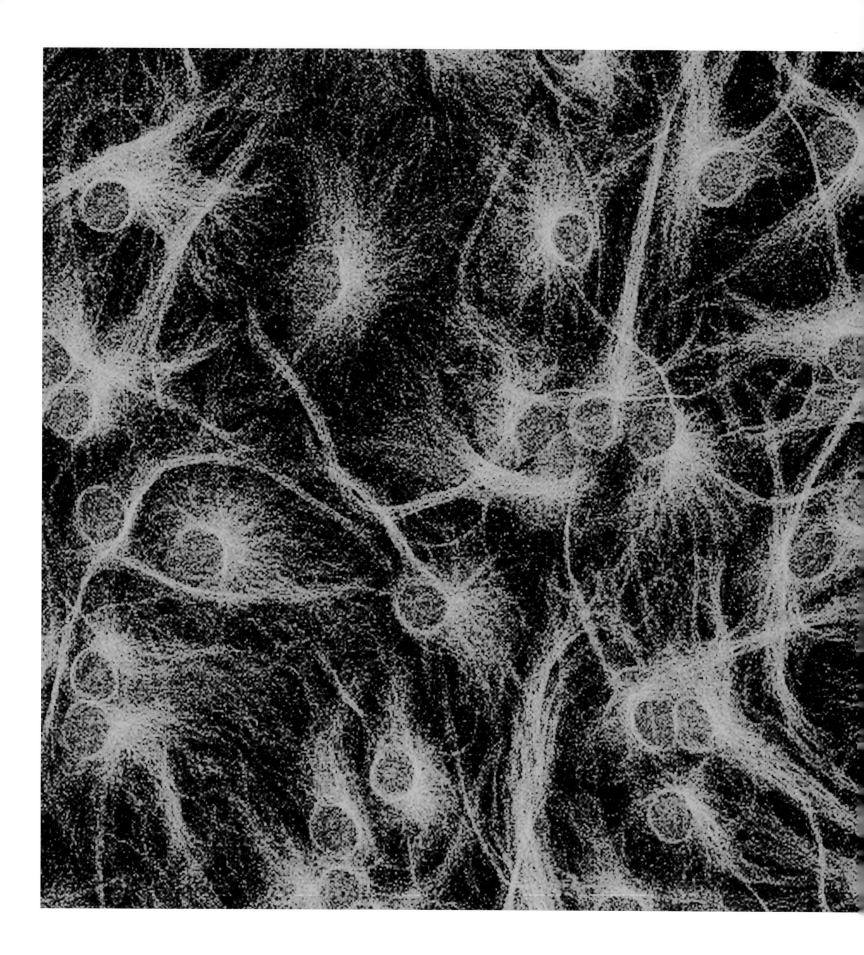

Zentrales Nervensystem
Le système nerveux central
The central nervous system
Sistema nervioso central

«Blut ist ein ganz besondrer Saft», wie schon Mephisto in Goethes *Faust* sagt. Die für uns lebenswichtige Flüssigkeit muss zirkulieren, um ihre Bestandteile in den ganzen Körper zu transportieren. Die größeren Blutgefäße im Kopf eines Tieres wurden hier mit Hilfe der Magnetresonanz-Angiographie sichtbar gemacht. Mit dieser faszinierenden Technik ist es möglich, auf bzw. in den Kopf des lebendigen Tieres zu blicken, das bei dieser nicht-invasiven Methode kaum mehr beansprucht wird als ein Patient bei einer Untersuchung. Die Farben machen deutlich, dass das Blut nahezu symmetrisch durch die Gefäße strömt. Anderenfalls wäre eine Verengung der Gefäße zu diagnostizieren. Menschen haben einen Blick für die Symmetrie. Es gelingt ihnen, Abweichungen davon rasch und genau zu erkennen.

Comme le fait observer Méphistophèles dans le *Faust* de Goethe, le sang, indispensable à la vie, doit circuler à travers tout l'organisme et porter dans toutes les parties du corps les éléments dont il est chargé. Ce que l'on voit ici, ce sont les gros vaisseaux qui cheminent à l'intérieur de la cavité crânienne d'un animal. La technique utilisée pour les mettre en évidence est l'angiographie à résonance magnétique. On voit d'en haut l'intérieur du crâne de l'animal vivant, que cette méthode non invasive permet d'examiner sans qu'on ait à effectuer sur lui beaucoup plus de manipulations que pour un être humain. Les couleurs montrent que le flux sanguin est pratiquement symétrique, ce qui permet d'exclure l'hypothèse d'un rétrécissement vasculaire. L'homme aime la symétrie. Il a tôt fait de repérer tout ce qui s'en écarte.

As observed by Mephisto in Goethe's *Faust,* 'blood is a most peculiar essence', and this vital bodily fluid has to circulate in order to transport its components around the body. In this image the major blood vessels in an animal's head have been rendered visible by means of a fascinating technique known as magnetic resonance angiography. The observer looks from above both at and into the head of the living animal, which in this non-invasive technique is disturbed only slightly more than a patient undergoing a physical examination. The colours show that the blood is flowing through the vessels in almost symmetrical fashion. Were this not so, a diagnosis of narrowing of the vessels would be made. Humans have a good eye for symmetry and are able to recognise deviations towards asymmetry rapidly and precisely.

La sangre es, como afirma Mefistófeles en el *Fausto* de Goethe, una esencia muy especial; y este líquido vital debe circular para transportar a todo el cuerpo sus elementos nutritivos. Pueden verse en la imagen los principales vasos sanguíneos que discurren por la cavidad craneal de un animal, gracias a una técnica fascinante, la angiografía por resonancia magnética nuclear. El observador puede contemplar desde arriba el interior del cráneo de un animal vivo, que se deja explorar sin problemas con este método incruento. Los colores muestran claramente que el flujo sanguíneo es prácticamente simétrico en los distintos vasos sanguíneos; de lo contrario, la asimetría resultante permitiría diagnosticar una estenosis vascular. Los seres humanos tenemos un sentido visual especial para la simetría, lo cual nos permite reconocer de forma rápida y precisa cualquier anomalía asimétrica.

Large blood vessels in a rat brain revealed by magnetic resonance angiography. Markus von Kienlin, Jürgen Fingerle, Stephanie Schoeppenthau, Thomas Bielser, Basil Kuennecke, Roche Basel.

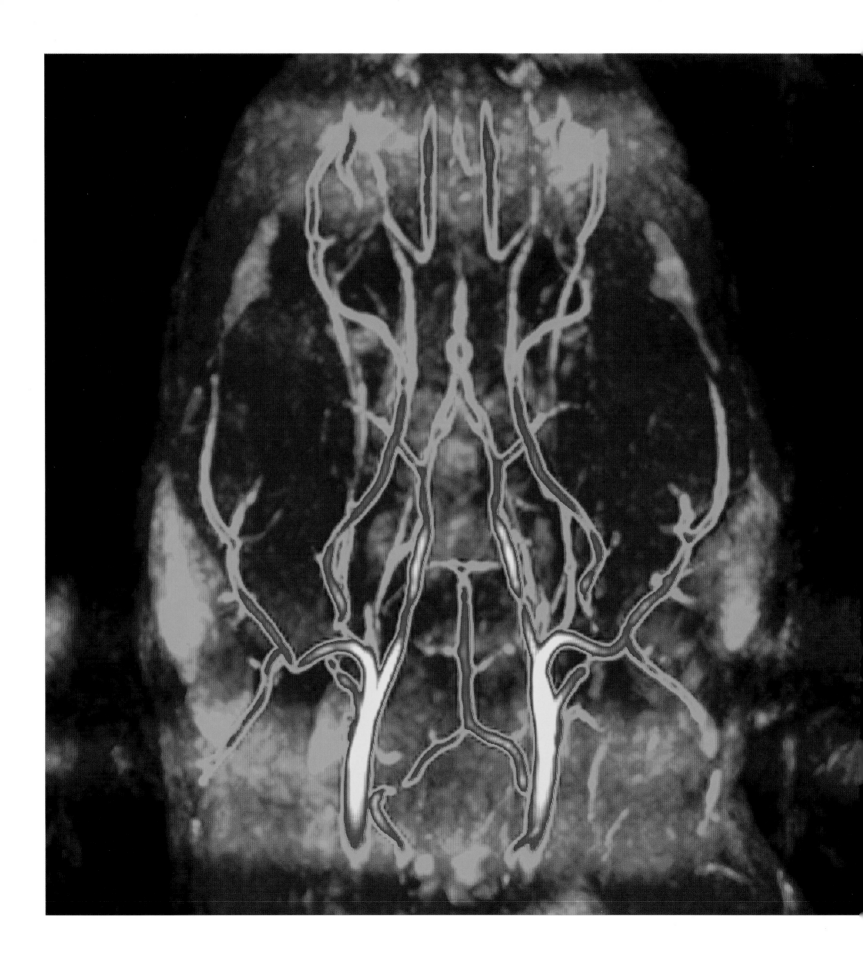

Zentrales Nervensystem
Le système nerveux central
The central nervous system
Sistema nervioso central

Kristalle können vielfältig erscheinen, selbst wenn sie aus den gleichen Bausteinen bestehen. Während des Heranwachsens bilden sie oftmals lange und nadelförmige Strukturen aus, doch hin und wieder zeigen sie kurze und eher rundliche Formen, denen Experten bescheinigen, im Detail hexagonal gebaut zu sein. Das in beiden Gebilden enthaltene Molekül hilft unserem Nervensystem, das Gedächtnis aufzubauen, dank dessen wir uns wahrscheinlich noch lange an dieses Bild erinnern. Besonders einprägsam ist das kreisförmige Blickfeld, da diese geschlossene Formation zu den Urbildern gehört, die Menschen in ihrer inneren Vorstellung entwickeln und in der Außenwelt finden. Zudem entsteht eine Spannung zwischen den von oben und den von unten wachsenden Kristallen: wir warten förmlich darauf, dass beide zusammentreffen. Kunsttheoretiker würden das einen fruchtbaren Moment nennen – mit einem Blick zu sehen, was vorher war und was nachher wird.

Même constitués de matériaux identiques, les cristaux peuvent revêtir des aspects très divers. Ils forment souvent, en grandissant, des structures effilées, en forme d'aiguille, mais il en existe aussi de plus courts et d'aspect plutôt arrondi, dont les experts disent qu'ils sont de structure hexagonale. Dans les deux cas, la molécule qu'ils contiennent est utilisée par le système nerveux pour bâtir la mémoire. Mais si nous en conservons longtemps l'image, ce n'est pas uniquement pour cette raison. L'œil aime, en effet, ce qui est rond. Cela fait partie des images primitives que l'homme forme à l'intérieur de lui-même. Qui plus est, on s'attend littéralement à ce que les cristaux du haut et ceux du bas se rejoignent, et cela donne à l'image l'attrait supplémentaire du mouvement. Elle saisit ce que les théoriciens de l'art appellent un moment fécond, où l'on voit tout de suite ce qui était et ce qui sera.

Crystals can assume a multiplicity of appearances, even when made of the same building blocks. As they grow, they often form long, needle-like structures, but occasionally they develop into short, rounded forms, the structure of which is referred to by experts as 'hexagonal'. In this image, the molecule contained in both forms helps our nervous system to build up memory. That will probably not be the only reason this image sticks in our minds, however: it also offers a circular field of view, and the circle is one of the archetypes we humans form within ourselves and encounter in the outside world. There is also a tension between the crystals growing from above and those growing from below, and we are held in suspense of a meeting of the two sides. The image captures what art theorists refer to as a 'fruitful moment' – we see at a glance both what preceded and what is to follow the instant of the image.

Los cristales, incluso formados por los mismos materiales, pueden adoptar multitud de formas. Al crecer forman con frecuencia largas estructuras espiculadas, pero de vez en cuando muestran también formas cortas y más redondeadas, de estructura íntima hexagonal, según afirman los especialistas. La molécula contenida en ambos tipos de formaciones contribuye en nuestro sistema nervioso a la memoria. Es probable que recordemos esta imagen no sólo por este motivo, sino también porque ofrece un campo visual circular, y el círculo es uno de los arquetipos o imágenes primitivas que el ser humano genera en su interior y reconoce en el mundo exterior. Puede percibirse, además, una tensión entre los cristales que crecen en los polos superior e inferior, que uno espera ver cómo terminan por unirse. Esta imagen capta lo que los teóricos del arte llaman un «momento fecundo», en el que una mirada basta para ver lo que ha sucedido y lo que habrá de suceder.

Crystals of neuronal calcium sensor-1. Polarising microscopy, Allan D'Arcy, Martine Stihle, Roche Basel.

Zentrales Nervensystem
Le système nerveux central
The central nervous system
Sistema nervioso central

Der unbekannte Stoff, der Menschen das Gedächtnis nimmt, kann im Experiment isoliert und in anderer Umgebung analysiert werden, um so seine Wirkung sichtbar zu machen. Das rundliche rote Gebilde, das unter dem Lichtmikroskop zu erkennen ist, stammt von einem Plaque, der sich im Gehirn ausbreitet und von einem Zentrum aus seine Fühler nach außen streckt. Er wirkt wie eine Schönheit, die uns in Schrecken versetzt. Den Untersuchungen, deren Ergebnis wir hier im Bild sehen, liegen hoch entwickelte genetische Techniken zugrunde, die das Übertragen von Genen und deren Steuerung einschließen.

La substance inconnue, qui prive peu à peu l'homme de mémoire, peut être isolée en laboratoire et analysée, de façon à en rendre visibles les méfaits. La formation rouge que permet de voir le microscope photonique provient d'une plaque formée de neurofilaments pathologiques, qui s'étendent dans le cerveau. L'image est belle, mais d'une beauté effrayante. Les investigations dont on voit ici le résultat mettent en jeu des techniques extrêmement sophistiquées, consistant notamment à introduire dans le patrimoine héréditaire d'un animal des gènes provenant d'un autre animal.

The unknown substance that robs human beings of their memory can be isolated and analysed in another environment in such a way as to render its action visible. The roundish red structure that can be seen under the light microscope corresponds to a plaque that is extending its feelers outward and thus spreading within the brain like some strange and terrifying, but at the same time beautiful, invader. The investigations that led to the production of this image involve highly complex genetic techniques, including the transfer and manipulation of genes.

La sustancia ignota que roba la memoria a las personas puede aislarse y analizarse en el laboratorio, con el fin de hacer visibles sus efectos. La estructura redondeada de color rojo reconocible al microscopio óptico corresponde a una placa senil que extiende sus prolongaciones para diseminarse por la corteza cerebral. La imagen es de una belleza aterradora. Los experimentos que ofrecen imágenes como ésta se basan en técnicas genéticas muy avanzadas, consistentes en la transferencia de genes humanos a un animal de laboratorio.

Senile plaque in the neocortex of a transgenic mouse (overexpressing hAPPswe and hPS2mut). Congo red staining and brightfield microscopy, Grayson Richards, Roche Basel.

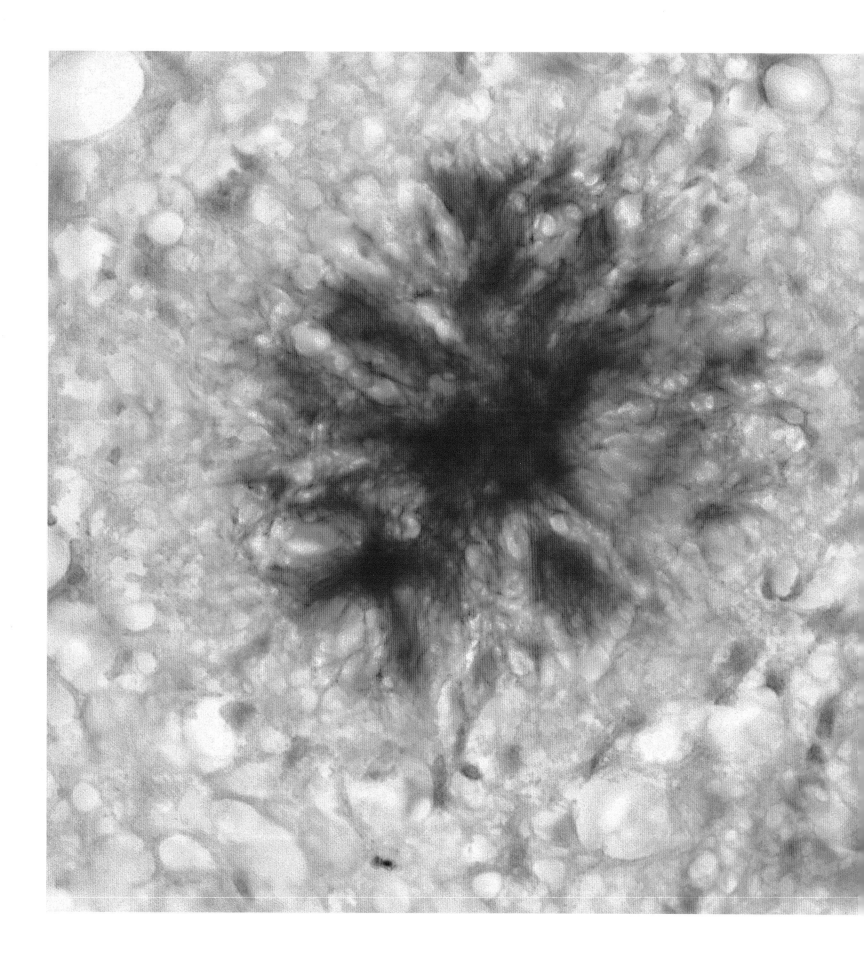

Zentrales Nervensystem
Le système nerveux central
The central nervous system
Sistema nervioso central

Die Alzheimerkrankheit, die nach heutigem Stand des Wissens im fortgeschrittenen Alter jeden treffen kann, stellt eine der größten Herausforderungen der Medizin dar. Indem sie unser Gedächtnis beeinträchtigt, lässt sie uns selbst gleichsam aus dem Leben zurücktreten. Während die Großhirnrinde schwindet, setzt die Vergesslichkeit ein, bis das Gedächtnis fast völlig erlischt. Die lichtmikroskopische Aufnahme zeigt in knapp zehnfacher Vergrößerung, wie es in einem zerrütteten Gehirn – genauer: in der Hirnrinde – aussehen kann. Von den drei Grundfarben Rot, Gelb und Blau weist vor allem das kalte Blau auf die befallenen Abschnitte, die senilen Plaques, im Nervengewebe hin. Die Hirnzellen, die sich gehäuft in der Nähe der Plaques zeigen, sind eisblau. Ein Maler hätte die Farbe nicht besser wählen können, um sie kenntlich zu machen.

L'un des plus grands défis qu'ait à relever la médecine est une maladie dont on sait qu'elle peut frapper toute personne ayant atteint un certain âge. S'attaquant à la mémoire, la maladie d'Alzheimer, puisque c'est d'elle qu'il s'agit, abolit le souvenir et ôte tous repères à ceux qui en sont victimes. Au fur et à mesure que le cortex cérébral s'atrophie, s'installe l'oubli, jusqu'à ce que la mémoire s'éteigne presque complètement. L'image que l'on voit ici a été prise au microscope photonique. Grossie à peine dix fois, elle montre les dégâts que cette maladie peut provoquer dans un cerveau ou, pour être précis, dans le cortex cérébral. Des trois couleurs fondamentales – rouge, jaune, bleu – le bleu est celle qui témoigne le plus visiblement des plaques séniles qui envahissent le tissu nerveux. Les neurones, dont on voit l'accumulation au voisinage des plaques, apparaissent dans un bleu glacial, qu'un peintre n'aurait pu mieux choisir pour les faire ressortir.

One of the major challenges facing medicine is a disease to which all elderly people are now believed to be potentially susceptible. This is Alzheimer's disease, which by impairing memory causes the affected individual almost to withdraw from life. Shrinking of the cerebral cortex is accompanied by increasing forgetfulness and ultimately leads to almost complete loss of memory. This light micrograph shows (at a magnification of only ten) the appearance of a devastated brain – or more precisely, cerebral cortex. Of the three primary colours, red, yellow and blue, the cold blue, in particular, indicates the position of the affected areas – known as senile plaques – in the brain tissue. The brain cells, which are present in increased numbers in the vicinity of the plaques, are ice-blue. A painter could scarcely have made a better choice of colour for distinguishing these cells.

Uno de los mayores retos de la medicina moderna es el planteado por una enfermedad que, en el estado actual de la ciencia, puede afectar a cualquier persona de edad avanzada. Me refiero a la enfermedad de Alzheimer, que deteriora la memoria y hurta al enfermo sus recuerdos y su conexión a la vida. Conforme el cerebro se atrofia, la memoria se reduce hasta llegar a desaparecer casi por completo. La fotografía tomada con un microscopio óptico de apenas 10 aumentos muestra el aspecto de un cerebro –más exactamente la corteza cerebral– afectado por la enfermedad. De los tres colores fundamentales –rojo, amarillo y azul–, este último sobre todo indica las zonas deterioradas del tejido nervioso, las llamadas «placas seniles». Las neuronas, que se amontonan en las proximidades de las placas seniles, son de color azul glacial; un pintor no hubiera podido escoger mejor los colores para destacarlas.

Increased MAO-B (red patches) in plaque-associated astrocytes in the temporal cortex of an Alzheimer's patient revealed by enzyme radioautography. Pseudocolour computer image, Grayson Richards, Roche Basel.

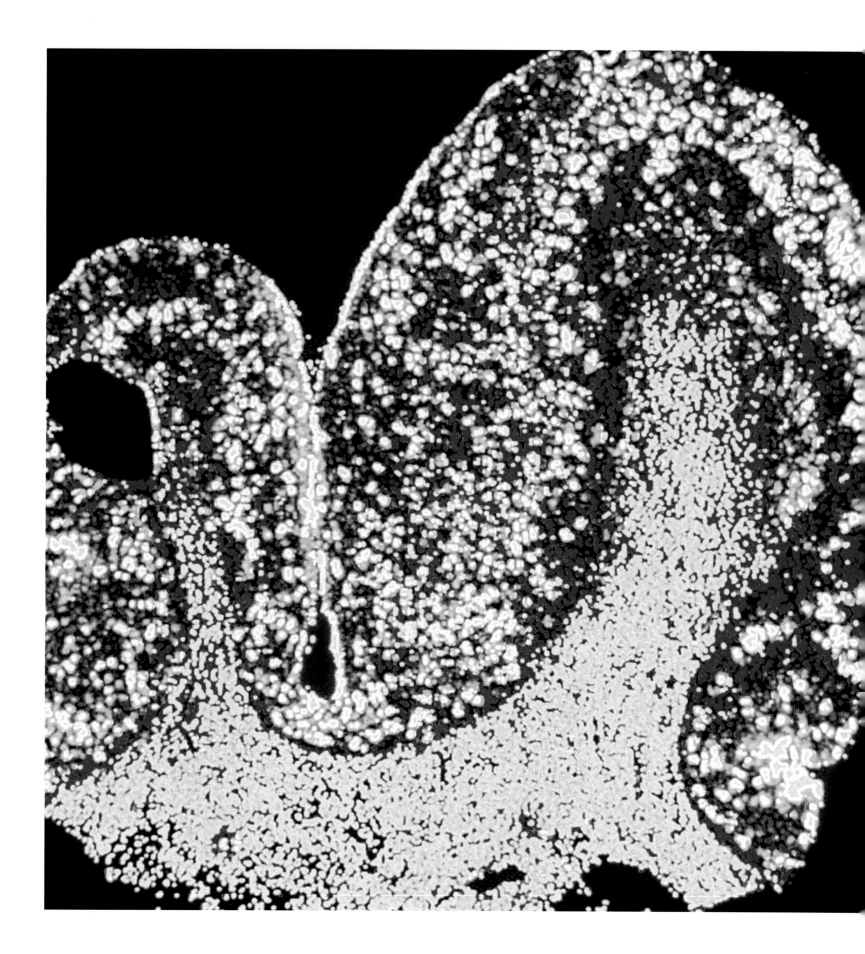

Zentrales Nervensystem
Le système nerveux central
The central nervous system
Sistema nervioso central

Astrozyten – so nennen Neurobiologen die Zellen des Nervensystems, die sich sternförmig strecken und auf diese Weise nicht nur weiten Kontakt suchen, sondern auch für enge Verflechtungen sorgen. Mit den modernen Methoden der Zellbiologie lassen sich diese vielfach verzweigten Einheiten des Lebens in künstlicher Umgebung erst kultivieren, dann analysieren und fotografieren. Zwar ist das Bild gestellt, aber die metallisch graue Farbe des Sterns entschädigt reichlich dafür. Der Stern rückt nahe an den Betrachter heran, da Blau als Hintergrund Ferne suggeriert.

Les astrocytes sont des cellules nerveuses de forme étoilée, qui envoient très loin leurs prolongements et forment des entrelacs très denses. Les scientifiques savent aujourd'hui élever en milieu artificiel, analyser et photographier ces unités fortement ramifiées de la vie. Il s'agit ici d'un astrocyte qui «prend la pose», mais comment lui en vouloir en voyant le beau gris métallique de l'étoile, que le bleu de l'arrière-plan, en suggérant l'éloignement, fait paraître encore plus proche du spectateur.

Astrocyte is the name given by neurobiologists to cells of the central nervous system that extend in star-like fashion not only to make distant contact, but also to create complex interconnections. With the aid of modern cell biology techniques, these extensively branched living entities can be cultivated in an artificial environment and then analysed and photographed. The image that we see here is thus 'posed'. However, the striking metallic grey colour of the star more than justifies this artifice. As a blue background always suggests distance, the star appears to be in the foreground.

Los astrocitos, así llamados por su forma estrellada que les permite generar contactos a distancia y formar una tupida red de interconexiones. Los métodos modernos de la biología celular permiten cultivar primero estas células tan ramificadas en un medio artificial, para luego analizarlas y fotografiarlas. Se trata, pues, de una imagen preparada, de estudio, pero el llamativo color gris metálico de la estrella compensa con creces este pequeño truco. Dado que los fondos azules sugieren lejanía, la estrella parece aún más próxima al observador.

Immunostaining of GFAP (glial fibrillary acidic protein) in neuronal cell culture (astrocytes). Confocal fluorescence microscopy, pseudo-3D image, Remo Hochstrasser, Roche Basel.

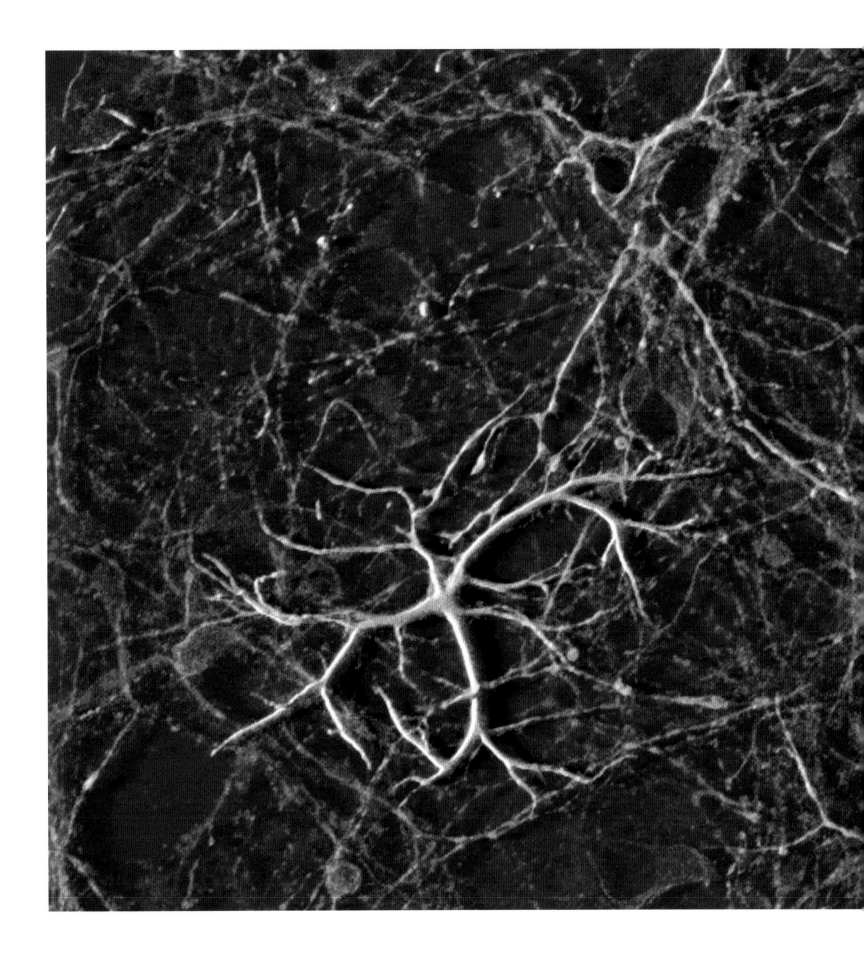

Zentrales Nervensystem
Le système nerveux central
The central nervous system
Sistema nervioso central

Kristalle haben es den Menschen schon immer angetan, nicht nur, weil sie mit ihren regelmäßigen Formen dem Auge Gelegenheit geben, Muster zu finden, sondern auch, weil sie wachsen können und damit eine Eigenschaft des Lebens selbst besitzen. Die Kristalle der Natur setzen sich gewöhnlich aus kleinen Molekülen wie Kohlenstoff oder Kochsalz zusammen. Die Wissenschaft kann Kristalle aus Proteinen, den Makromolekülen des Lebens, herstellen – wachsen lassen, wie die Experten sagen. Mit Hilfe von Proteinen kann eine Zelle die biochemischen Reaktionen des Lebens in Gang setzen und halten. Auf dem Bild schillert die Farbvielfalt von Proteinkristallen, die zur Familie der Cyclophiline gehören. Mit ihrer Hilfe hält sich das Nervensystem in Form.

L'homme a toujours été fasciné par les cristaux. S'il apprécie la régularité de leur construction ainsi que les combinaisons de motifs géométriques qu'ils offrent à l'œil, il est sensible aussi à l'idée que ce sont des formations capables de croissance et possédant donc une des qualités de la vie. Les cristaux que l'on rencontre dans la nature se composent généralement de petites molécules de carbone ou de sodium. Ceux que l'on voit ici, brillant d'un vif éclat, ont été élevés dans des conditions purement expérimentales, et il ne s'agit pas de molécules de carbone ou de sodium, mais de cristaux de protéines appartenant à la famille des cyclophilines, substances nécessaires au bon état du système nerveux.

Crystals have always held an attraction for humans. Not just because they are regular in construction and give the eye an opportunity to identify patterns, but also because, having the capacity to grow, they possess one of the characteristics of living things. Naturally occurring crystals are generally composed of small molecules such as carbon or sodium chloride (common salt). Scientists have succeeded in making – 'growing', in technical jargon – crystals out of proteins, the macromolecules cells use to initiate and maintain biochemical reactions. This image shows the shimmering and varied colours of crystals of the cyclophilin family of proteins, which help to keep the nervous system functioning correctly.

Los cristales han fascinado desde siempre al ser humano, no sólo por la regularidad de su construcción que permite al ojo identificar motivos geométricos, sino también porque poseen una de las características básicas de la vida: la capacidad de crecer. Los cristales naturales suelen estar formados por moléculas de pequeño tamaño, como el carbono o la sal común (cloruro sódico), pero los científicos pueden crear también cristales a partir de las proteínas, macromoléculas de las que se sirven las células para llevar a cabo las reacciones químicas vitales. En la imagen puede apreciarse la policromía irisada de los cristales de ciclofilina A, una proteína del sistema nervioso.

Crystals of cyclophilin-A, polarising microscopy. Allan D'Arcy, Martine Stihle, Roche Basel.

Zentrales Nervensystem
Le système nerveux central
The central nervous system
Sistema nervioso central

Leben und Denken sind Bewegung, und das Gehirn gerät in Schwierigkeiten, wenn Ablagerungen (Plaques) seine Dynamik erst einschränken und dann aufhalten. So beginnt die Alzheimerkrankheit. Das hochauflösende Instrument der Transmissionselektronenmikroskopie ermöglicht uns zu sehen, was dabei im Detail geschieht. Proteine bilden Fibrillen, und diese Strukturen scheinen ein festes Netz zu spannen. Wir können uns bildlich vorstellen, dass sich darin die Gedanken verfangen. In diesem Netzwerk von Verknüpfungen stecken auch Ansatzpunkte für neue Arzneimittel.

Vivre et penser sont deux choses qui participent du mouvement. Aussi le cerveau peine-t-il lorsque des plaques, c'est-à-dire des dépôts de matières pathologiques, viennent d'abord ralentir, puis empêcher son activité. C'est pourtant ce qui se produit quand commence la maladie d'Alzheimer. Grâce à son fort pouvoir de résolution, la microscopie électronique à transmission permet d'étudier ce processus dans le détail. Des protéines donnent naissance à des fibrilles, lesquelles forment comme un filet aux mailles rigides, où l'on imagine sans peine que puissent rester accrochées les pensées. Mais dans ce vaste réseau d'interconnexions se trouvent aussi les cibles des futurs médicaments.

Life and thought consist of movement, and the brain gets into difficulty if plaques restrict and ultimately stop its activity. This, however, is precisely what happens when Alzheimer's disease begins. The high-resolution technique of transmission electron microscopy allows us to see the details of this process. Proteins form fibrils that seem to interlock to form a solid mesh, in which it is easy to imagine thoughts becoming entangled. At the same time, however, this interlocked mesh also contains potential points of attack for new drugs.

Tanto el vivir como el pensar es movimiento. El cerebro se halla en una situación comprometida cuando la formación de placas seniles limita gravemente su actividad o la paraliza por completo. Y esto es precisamente lo que sucede en la enfermedad de Alzheimer. El gran poder de resolución de la microscopia electrónica de transmisión nos permite contemplar en detalle lo que sucede en tales placas. Las proteínas forman fibrillas que parecen tejer una espesa red en la que uno, metafóricamente, imagina atrapados los pensamientos. En esta intrincada red, no obstante, se hallan también los objetivos moleculares de los medicamentos del futuro.

Protein fibrils of beta-amyloid peptide revealed by transmission electron microscopy. Françoise Gerber, Claudia Richardson, Bernd Bohrmann, Roche Basel.

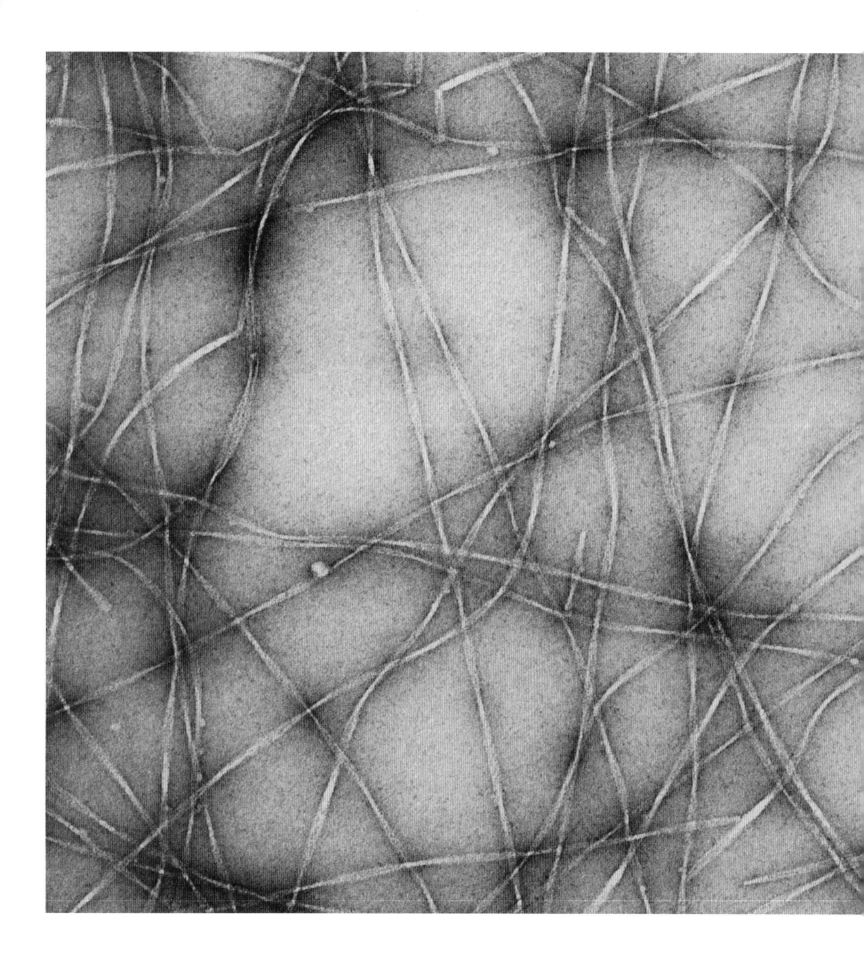

Zentrales Nervensystem
Le système nerveux central
The central nervous system
Sistema nervioso central

Wie Sterne leuchten die Zellen einer Netzhaut. Die Astrozyten treten nicht als Nervenzellen in Erscheinung, sondern übernehmen andere verbindende Funktionen. Ihre gleichmäßige und regelhaft wirkende Verteilung ist unmittelbar zu erkennen, und das menschliche Auge beginnt nach der Gestaltung ihrer Anordnung zu suchen, die darauf angelegt zu sein scheint, unnötigen Berührungen aus dem Weg zu gehen.

Elles brillent comme des étoiles. Astrocytes ne sont d'ailleurs pas des cellules nerveuses, mais des cellules qui forment un tissu interstitiel jouant un rôle très important dans les échanges hémocérébraux. Semblant obéir à des règles précises, la régularité de leur disposition saute pour ainsi dire aux yeux, suscitant immédiatement en nous une interrogation sur les causes de cette régularité. Serait-ce pour éviter tout contact inutile avec les cellules voisines?

These cells from a retina shine like stars. Rather than acting as nerve cells as such, astrocytes have supporting functions. Their even and seemingly regular distribution is immediately apparent, and the human eye starts to look for patterns in their distribution, the purpose of which seems to be to minimise contact.

Como estrellas relucen las células de la retina. Astrocitos no son neuronas, sino células de apoyo del sistema nervioso. Su distribución uniforme y regular salta de inmediato a la vista, y el ojo humano comienza a buscar patrones de distribución, cuya finalidad parece ser evitar todo contacto inútil con las células vecinas.

Astrocytes from a cat retina. Fluorescence microscopy, Heinz Wässle, Max Planck Institute for Brain Research, Frankfurt am Main.

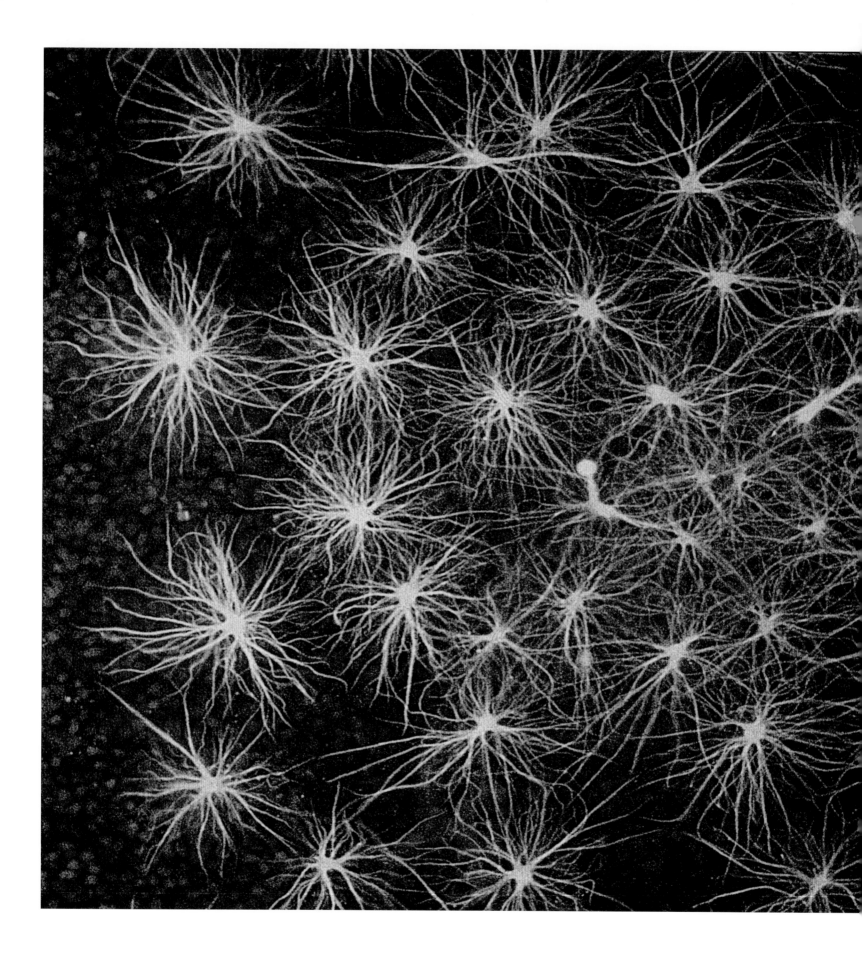

> I am certain of nothing
> but the holiness of the heart's
> affection and the truth
> of imagination –
> what the imagination seizes
> as beauty must be truth –
> whether it existed before or not.

John Keats (1795 – 1821)

Vaskuläre Erkrankungen

Dem Herzen nah

Les maladies cardio-vasculaires

Près du cœur

Vascular diseases

Close to the heart

Enfermedades vasculares

Junto al corazón

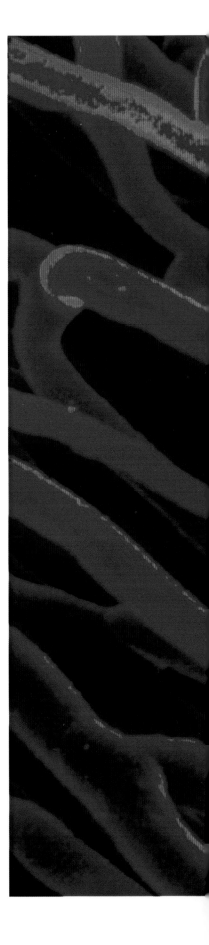

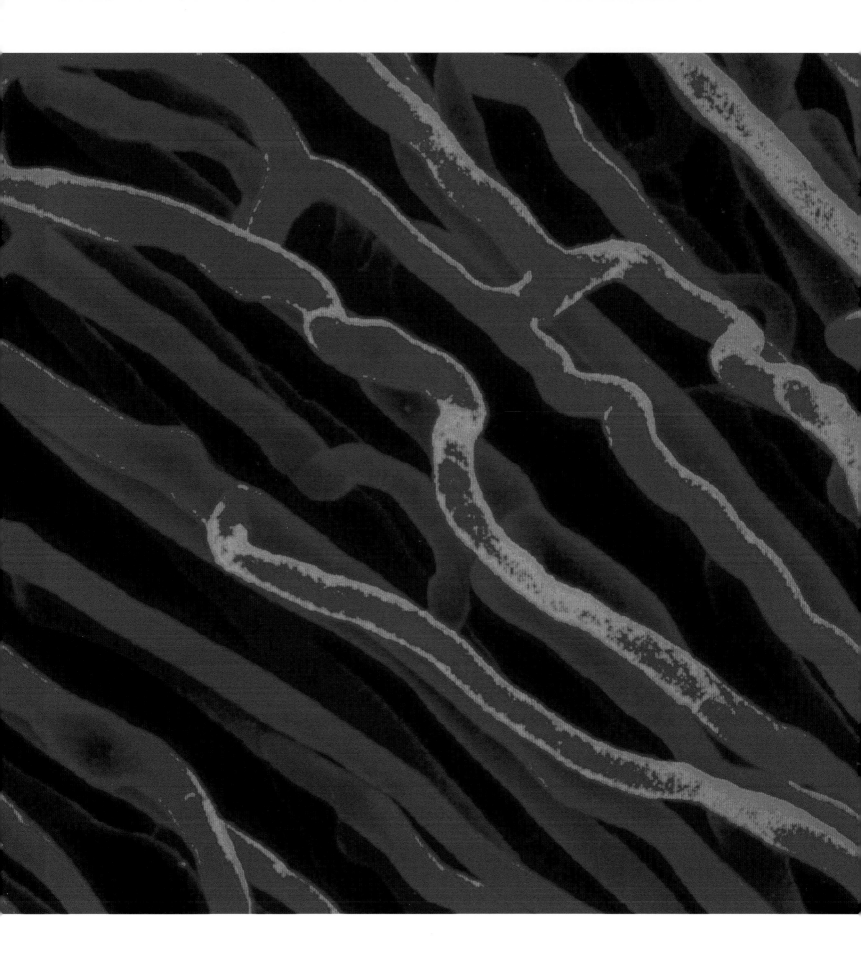

Dem Herzen nah

Près du cœur

Das Besondere an unserem Blut, dem roten Lebenselixier, lässt sich an mindestens zwei Qualitäten erkennen. Einerseits muss es gut und ungestört in den Gefäßen, die den Körper durchziehen, fließen können, andererseits muss es so rasch wie möglich erstarren und gerinnen, sobald es durch eine Verletzung aus dem Körper austritt. Wie gefährdet die erste Eigenschaft – der Lebensfluss – ist, belegen die Statistiken, nach denen die häufigste Todesursache in den industrialisierten Länden die Gefäßkrankheiten sind. Und wie präzise die zweite Eigenschaft – die Gerinnung – reguliert werden muss, zeigen Herzinfarkt oder Schlaganfall. Wenn die Verstopfung zur falschen Zeit einsetzt und der Blutfluss plötzlich stockt, ist das Leben gefährdet.

Übrigens, in der Antike wurde vielfach angenommen, dass es das Herz ist, mit dem der Mensch denkt. Diese Vermutung findet sich zum Beispiel bei Aristoteles, der dem Gehirn nur die Kühlung des Körpers zutraute. Dass wir mit dem Herzen denken, glauben wir heute zwar nicht mehr, aber mit dem Herzen zu verstehen, dies gehört immer noch zu den Wünschen, die man äussern darf – sogar den exakten Naturwissenschaften gegenüber.

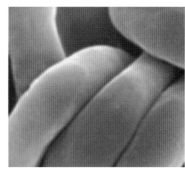

Pour bien remplir son rôle, le sang, élixir de vie, doit pouvoir circuler librement, et sans rencontrer d'obstacles, à l'intérieur des vaisseaux sanguins qui parcourent tout le corps. Mais qu'une blessure lui permette soudain de s'échapper vers le dehors, il faut qu'aussitôt il se fige et coagule. Pour ce qui est de l'importance du flux sanguin, les statistiques nous la rappellent avec insistance: les maladies cardio-vasculaires sont la première cause de mortalité du monde industrialisé. Quant à la coagulation du sang, toute personne informée de ce qu'est un infarctus du myocarde ou une attaque cérébrale sait combien elle doit être réglée avec précision et ce qu'il peut en coûter si un caillot de sang vient intempestivement à boucher une artère, privant d'oxygène le territoire normalement irrigué par elle.

Beaucoup d'Anciens croyaient d'ailleurs que c'est avec le cœur que l'on pense. Exemple: Aristote, pour qui le rôle du cerveau se bornait à réguler la température du corps. Si nous ne croyons plus, aujourd'hui, que l'on pense avec le cœur, nous continuons néanmoins de souhaiter – n'en déplaise aux sciences exactes – qu'il soit au moins permis de comprendre avec le cœur.

PP. 36/37: Vascular cast, mammalian, heart endocardium. Scanning electron microscopy, CMSP.

Close to the heart

Junto al corazón

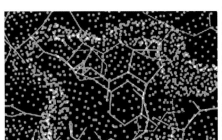

The special nature of our blood, the red elixir of life, can be seen from at least two of its characteristics. On the one hand, it must be able to flow smoothly and without interruption in the blood vessels that permeate the body, while on the other it must set into a clot as soon as possible after escaping from an injured blood vessel. The fragility of the first characteristic – the flow of blood that maintains life – is clear to anyone who is aware that cardiovascular diseases are the most common cause of death in industrialised countries. And the precision with which the second characteristic – coagulation – has to be regulated is clear to anyone who has learnt a little about heart attacks and strokes. Life can be easily endangered when blood coagulates at the wrong time and the flow of blood to vital organs suddenly stops.

Interestingly, in ancient times it was commonly supposed that human beings thought with their hearts. This belief was shared by Aristotle, who considered the brain to be responsible only for keeping the body cool. Though we no longer believe that human beings think with their hearts, we still regard it as normal to want to understand – and even to understand the natural sciences – with our hearts.

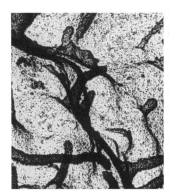

La calidad especial de nuestro rojo elixir de la vida se basa al menos en dos propiedades esenciales. Por un lado, la sangre debe fluir correctamente y sin problemas por los vasos que recorren todo el cuerpo; y por otro, debe poder coagularse rápidamente en cuanto se produce una herida. Hasta qué punto se halla amenazada la primera propiedad –la fluidez– lo sabe cualquiera que conozca las estadísticas de las principales causas de muerte en los países industralizados, encabezadas por las enfermedades cardiovasculares. Y con qué precisión debe regularse la segunda propiedad –la coagulación– lo sabe cualquiera que haya leído algo sobre el infarto de miocardio o la apoplejía. Es fácil adivinar lo que sucede cuando la sangre se coagula en el momento equivocado: el flujo sanguíneo se detiene de repente y ello puede causar la muerte.

En la Antigüedad, además, se admitía ampliamente que el corazón era la sede del pensamiento en el ser humano. Así lo creía, por ejemplo, Aristóteles, para quien la misión del cerebro consistía únicamente en mantener frío el cuerpo. Hoy ya no nadie cree que pensemos con el corazón, pero ver y entender con el corazón sigue siendo uno de nuestros deseos, incluso en relación con las ciencias naturales.

Das blaue Rund stellt eine zweihundertfach vergrößerte Arterie dar, so wie sie sich dem Beobachter zeigt, der durch ein Lichtmikroskop schaut. Man kann sich gut vorstellen, wie leicht sich Teile aus dem vorbeiströmenden Blut, die direkt mit der Wand in Berührung kommen, an der ornamentartigen Innenlinie verfangen können. Dabei entstehen Ablagerungen, die das Bild im rechten Teil zeigt, und die als Atherosklerose bekannt sind.

L'anneau bleu que l'on voit sur cette image au microscope photonique est la lumière d'une artère sous fort grossissement multiplié par deux cent. La face interne, très ornementale, du vaisseau paraît avoir été conçue pour retirer du sang qui coule en lui les éléments entrant en contact direct avec sa paroi. On voit, sur le bord de droite du vaisseau, les dépôts qui en résultent et qui sont constitutifs de l'arthérosclérose.

The blue ring represents an artery magnified two hundred times, as it appears to someone looking down a light microscope. The seemingly decorative inner line appears capable of holding on to any blood components that come into direct contact with the vessel wall as the blood flows by. This gives rise to deposits – such as that seen on the righthand side of the ring – known as atherosclerosis.

Este anillo azulado corresponde a una arteria aumentada doscientas veces, tal como puede verse a través de un microscopio óptico. La ornamentada línea interior parece hecha a propósito para retener las partículas del torrente circulatorio que entren en contacto directo con la pared arterial. Se forman así depósitos o placas de ateroma –como la que puede apreciarse en la parte derecha de la imagen–, responsables de la ateroesclerosis.

Mesenteric artery. Light microscopy, Bruno Wessner, Roland Krauer, Bernd Bohrmann, Roche Basel.

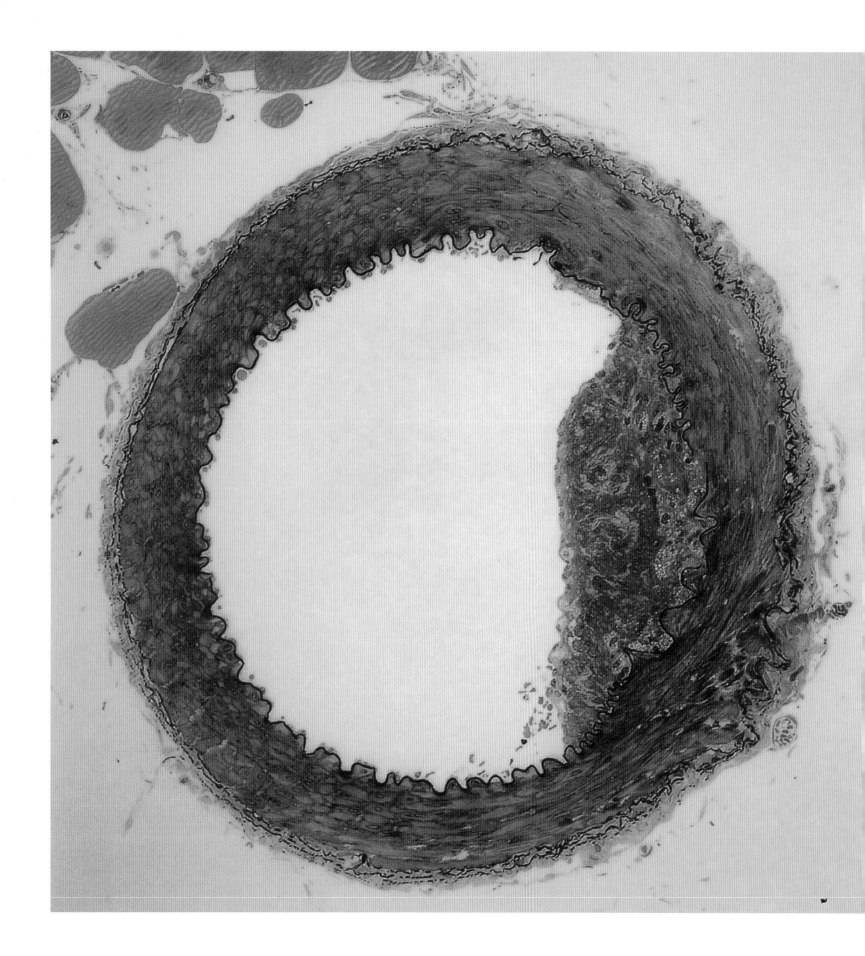

Wenn es nicht die rote und grüne Farbe im Bild gäbe, hätte man den Eindruck, einige Wolken zu sehen, die verstreut über eine graue Ebene ziehen. Der räumliche Eindruck kommt durch die Pseudo-3-D-Darstellung zustande. Die menschliche Wahrnehmung sieht die dunkel projizierten Schattenflächen als reale Gegebenheiten an, die das Gehirn dann als Teil einer dreidimensionalen Welt interpretiert. Die bunte Wolke besteht aus rot angefärbten Blutplättchen und grün angefärbten Leukozyten, die sich zu einem potenziell lebensbedrohlichen Blutpfropfen (Thrombus) verklebt haben.

N'étaient le rouge et le vert, on aurait l'impression de voir des formations nuageuses étirant leur masse au-dessus d'une plaine grise. L'effet de profondeur qui émane de cette représentation en pseudo 3D est dû au fait que le regard perçoit les parties sombres, qui sont en fait des ombres projetées, comme une réalité et qu'il suggère au cerveau d'appréhender ce que voit l'œil comme s'il s'agissait d'un univers en trois dimensions. Les «nuages» sont constitués de plaquettes sanguines, colorées en rouge, et de globules blancs, colorés en vert, qui se sont agglutinés, formant un thrombus (masse de sang coagulé) qui pourrait entraîner la mort par oblitération d'un vaisseau.

Were it not for the red and green colours in this image, we might think we were looking at scattered clouds drifting over a grey plain. The impression of spatial depth created here is known as a pseudo-3-D effect, the projected dark shaded areas being perceived by the human eye as real and thus interpreted by the brain as part of a three-dimensional world. The brightly coloured cloud is made up of red-stained platelets and green-stained leucocytes which have aggregated to form a potentially life-threatening thrombus.

De no ser por los colores rojo y verde, uno tendría la impresión de estar contemplando unas nubes que se desplazan sobre un plano gris. Esta impresión espacial corresponde a una «representación seudotridimensional» en la que la percepción humana interpreta como sombras reales las superficies oscuras, y sugiere al cerebro un mundo tridimensional. La nube bicromática está formada en realidad por plaquetas teñidas de rojo y leucocitos teñidos de verde aglutinados en un trombo o coágulo sanguíneo potencialmente mortal.

Immunostained thrombus. Confocal fluorescence microscopy, Remo Hochstrasser, Roche Basel.

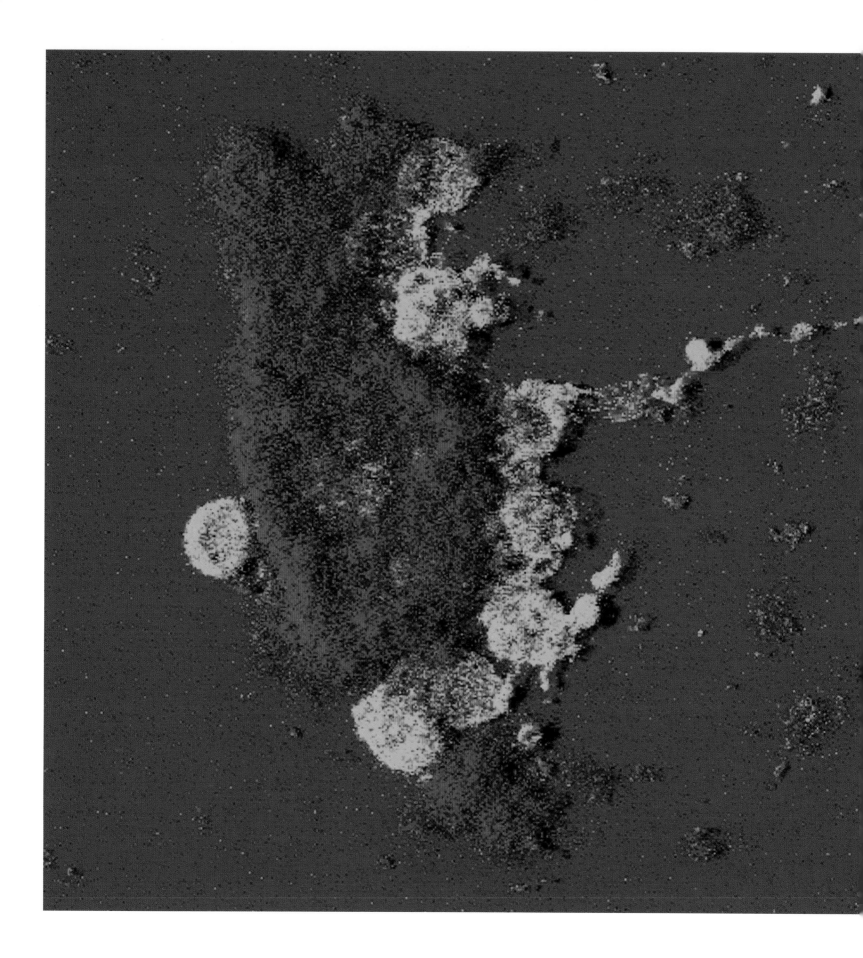

Die Blutgerinnung ist kein passiver Vorgang. Sie geschieht mit Hilfe zahlreicher Proteine, die als Faktoren bezeichnet werden. Sie sind einzeln durchnummeriert und bilden zusammen eine Kaskade, die den Blutgerinnungsvorgang Schritt für Schritt verstärkt. Der mikroskopische, molekulare Prozess führt zu einer makroskopischen, spürbaren Wirkung: der Gerinnung. Im Mittelpunkt zahlreicher Forschungsarbeiten steht der Faktor VII, der mit gentechnischer Hilfe in großem Umfang produziert werden kann. Um seine Struktur zu bestimmen, wird der Faktor VII kristallisiert. Besonders eindrucksvoll erscheinen die Kristalle unter dem blauen Licht eines polarisierten Mikroskops. Immer wieder erstaunt die Gradlinigkeit und die Regelmässigkeit, mit der sich biologische Gebilde erfassen lassen.

La coagulation du sang n'est pas un processus passif. Elle met en jeu de nombreuses protéines, ou facteurs de coagulation, numérotés de I à XIII. La conjonction de ces facteurs met en route une cascade de phénomènes biochimiques ayant pour effet d'intensifier le processus. Sous leur action, une cause microscopique (moléculaire) produit un effet macroscopique (tangible), qui est la coagulation. La recherche s'intéresse particulièrement au facteur VII, que le génie génétique permet de produire en grandes quantités. Pour en étudier la structure, on le fait passer à la forme cristalline. Les cristaux forment sous la lumière bleue d'un microscope polarisant une image saisissante, frappant par la linéarité et la régularité avec lesquelles se présentent les formations biologiques.

Blood coagulation is an active process involving a series of proteins known as coagulation factors. These are individually numbered and together form a cascade that culminates in blood coagulation. The microscopic (molecular) process in which they participate leads to a macroscopic (visible) effect, namely coagulation. Much recent research has focused on factor VII, which can be manufactured on a large scale using recombinant DNA technology. In order to elucidate its structure, factor VII is crystallised. The particularly striking appearance of the crystals shown here is due to the blue light of a polarising microscope. The linearity and regularity with which biological structures can be imaged never ceases to astound.

La coagulación de la sangre no es en absoluto un proceso pasivo. En él intervienen multitud de proteínas conocidas como «factores de la coagulación» (numerados del I al XIII), que actúan en cascada. Gracias a ellos, una causa molecular microscópica desemboca en un efecto macroscópico perceptible, como es el coágulo. Muchas investigaciones giran en torno al factor VII, que la ingeniería genética permite hoy obtener en grandes cantidades. Para poder determinar su estructura, es preciso cristalizar antes el factor VII. Especialmente impresionantes son estos cristales cuando se contemplan bajo la luz azul de un microscopio de polarización. Sorprende una y otra vez la perfección rectilínea y la regularidad que pueden adoptar las estructuras biológicas.

Crystals of recombinant factor VII. Polarising microscopy, Allan D'Arcy, Martine Stihle, Roche Basel.

Das tropfenförmige, filigrane Gebilde, das seine Fühler strahlenartig in alle Richtungen ausstreckt, ist eine Zelle, die in der Pharmaindustrie zur Produktion von Wirkstoffen genutzt wird. Fachleute bezeichnen sie mit der Abkürzung CHO (Chinese hamster ovary), da sie urspünglich einmal aus dem Gewebe eines Hamsters isoliert wurde. Die Zelle ist durch ein auf sie übertragenes Gen in die Lage versetzt worden, ein Protein herzustellen, das gewöhnlich auf der Oberfläche von Blutzellen, den Blutplättchen oder Thrombozyten, sitzt. Die Aufnahme entstand mit Hilfe der raffinierten Technik der Transmissionselektronenmikroskopie, für die die Zellen zunächst mit einem Metall, in diesem Fall Platin, bedampft werden.

Cette structure filigranée en forme de goutte, qui darde ses antennes comme des rayons, est une cellule à laquelle a été donné le nom de Chinese hamster ovary (CHO), parce que c'est chez un hamster qu'elle a été primitivement isolée. L'intérêt que lui porte l'industrie pharmaceutique tient au fait qu'on peut lui transférer un gène la rendant capable de produire une protéine que l'on trouve normalement à la surface des plaquettes sanguines. La technique utilisée pour ce cliché est la microscopie électronique de transmission, que précède une métallisation de l'échantillon, par exemple au platine.

The delicate, drop-like structure stretching its feelers out like rays in all directions is a cell that is used in the pharmaceutical industry for the production of medicines. Scientists refer to it as a CHO – Chinese hamster ovary – cell, as it belongs to a line of cells that was originally isolated from the ovary of a Chinese hamster. Transfer of a specific gene to this cell has enabled it to produce a protein that is normally found on the surface of platelets, a special type of blood cell. This image was produced using a sophisticated technique known as transmission electron microscopy, which is performed after evaporation of a metal such as platinum onto the cells.

Esta estructura en forma de gota, de la que parten a modo de filigrana finas radiaciones en todas direcciones, es una célula utilizada en la industria farmacéutica para la producción de principios activos. Los especialistas se refieren a ella con las siglas CHO (del inglés Chinese hamster ovary, por haberse aislado originalmente del ovario de un hámster). Tras insertarle un gen de otra especie, la célula se halla capacitada para sintetizar una proteína que, en condiciones normales, se encuentra en la superficie de las plaquetas sanguíneas. Esta microfotografía se obtuvo mediante microscopia electrónica de transmisión tras vaporización de las células con platino.

Transfected CHO (Chinese hamster ovary) cell. Transmission electron microscopy, Bruno Wessner, Roland Krauer, Bernd Bohrmann, Roche Basel.

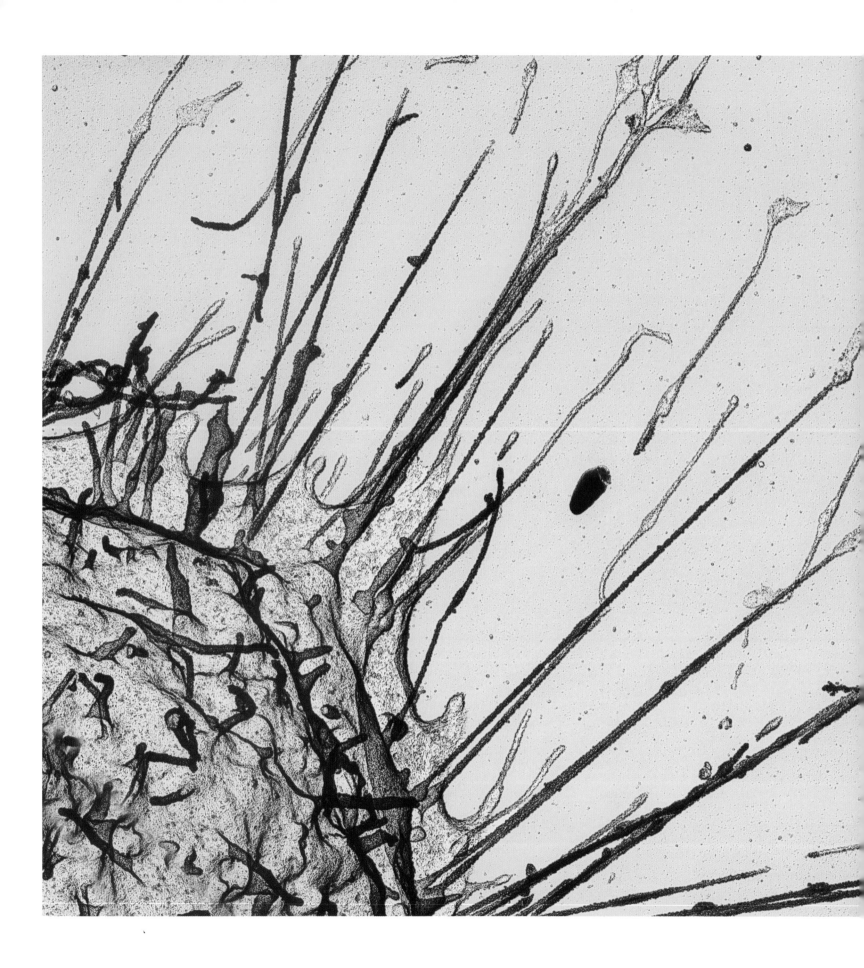

Aus Proteinkristallen lassen sich über viele Zwischenschritte Strukturmodelle eines Gerinnungsfaktors ableiten. Modelle werden nicht nur von etwas gemacht, sie werden auch immer für etwas gemacht. In diesem Fall soll das Modell des Gerinnungsfaktors VIIa zeigen, wie eng andere Moleküle der Zelle an ihn heranrücken können. Mit der in Punkten dargestellten Umhüllung – einer so genannten Connolly-Oberfläche – tritt der Faktor mit einem anderen Molekül, oder auch einem Medikament, in Kontakt. Diese Kenntnis der Struktur hilft, Angriffspunkte für Wirkstoffe zu finden.

Partant des cristaux de protéine, il est possible de dériver, moyennant plusieurs étapes intermédiaires, des modèles de la structure d'un facteur de coagulation. Quand des chercheurs construisent un modèle, c'est toujours dans un but d'étude et de démonstration. Le modèle du facteur de coagulation VIIa présenté ici sert à mettre en évidence l'étroitesse des rapports de voisinage pouvant exister entre ce facteur et d'autres molécules de la cellule. On appelle surface de Connolly l'enveloppement figuré ici par des points. Il s'agit de la surface grâce à laquelle le facteur de coagulation va pouvoir se lier à une autre molécule, qui pourrait aussi être un médicament. Les modèles qu'établissent les chercheurs permettent de sélectionner des cibles destinées à des substances actives.

Starting with protein crystals models of the structure of coagulation factor VIIa can be produced through a large number of intermediate steps. Models are always made for a purpose, in this case to show how closely this molecule can be approached by others in the cell. The coating of the molecule, seen here as a series of dots, is known as the 'Connolly surface'. This is the surface via which the coagulation factor comes into contact with other molecules, including drugs. Knowing the structure of such molecules helps in the search for targets for new drugs.

A partir de cristales de proteínas puede determinarse, pasando por multitud de pasos intermedios, la estructura de un factor de la coagulación. Estos modelos moleculares no sólo se hacen de algo, sino también para algo. En el caso de la imagen, este modelo del factor VIIa se utilizó para comprobar hasta qué punto podían aproximarse a él otras moléculas de la célula. Los puntos marcan la llamada superficie de Connolly, que representa la superficie de contacto entre el factor de la coagulación y otra molécula (p. ej., un medicamento). Este dato resulta muy útil para escoger los puntos de acción de los principios activos.

Protein structure of coagulation factor VIIa. Frank Grams, David Banner, Roche Basel.

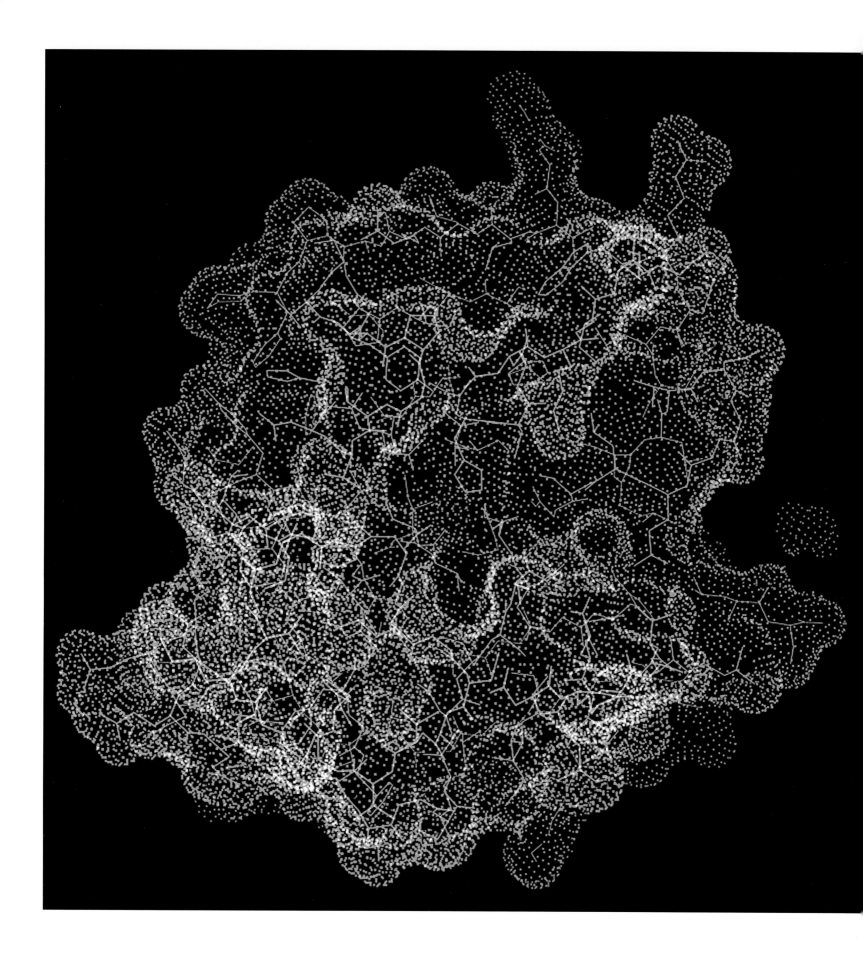

Ein einzelnes rotes Blutkörperchen, umhüllt von den Wänden eines schlanken Gefäßes – einer so genannten Kapillare. Die abgebildete Kapillare unterstützt die Blutversorgung des Zentralen Nervensystems. Auffällig ist die glatte Form der Blutzelle. Der grüne Ring, der den roten Kreis einfängt, lässt hingegen zahlreiche Strukturen, so genannte Organellen, erkennen. Dank der Technik, die mikroskopische Strukturen rund fünfzigtausendfach vergrößern kann, entsteht ein Bild, in dem sich die Gegensätze von Form und Farbe gegenseitig steigern und das unserem Auge zeigt, was ihm von Natur aus nicht zugedacht ist.

Globule rouge enveloppé par les parois d'un vaisseau capillaire participant à l'irrigation sanguine du système nerveux central. On est frappé par la forme parfaitement lisse de cette cellule sanguine, apparemment vierge de toute structure interne. L'anneau vert qui entoure le cercle rouge, en comporte, lui, de nombreuses, que l'on appelle des organelles. Grâce au miracle de la technique, qui permet de grossir une cinquantaine de milliers de fois les structures microscopiques, on obtient une image qui accentue le contraste entre la forme et la couleur, offrant ainsi à nos yeux un spectacle qui ne leur était pas naturellement destiné.

An individual red blood cell within a narrow blood vessel, or capillary. The capillary shown here helps to supply blood to the central nervous system. A striking feature is the smoothness of the blood cell. By contrast, the green ring that surrounds the red circle is seen to possess many fine structures, known as organelles. The technique used here, which can magnify microscopic structures by a factor of about fifty thousand, produces an image in which contrasts of form and colour reinforce each other, and our eyes see something that Nature did not intend them to see.

Un solo glóbulo rojo rodeado por las paredes de un capilar sanguíneo destinado a la irrigación del sistema nervioso central. Llama la atención la uniformidad del glóbulo rojo. En el anillo verde que rodea al círculo encarnado, en cambio, pueden reconocerse numerosos orgánulos. La técnica, que permite aumentar 50.000 veces las estructuras microscópicas, revela a nuestro ojo lo que la naturaleza le había ocultado, y nos ofrece una imagen en la que los contrastes de forma y color se potencian recíprocamente.

Red blood cell in a capillary. Transmission electron microscopy, copyright Denis Kunkel Microscopy.

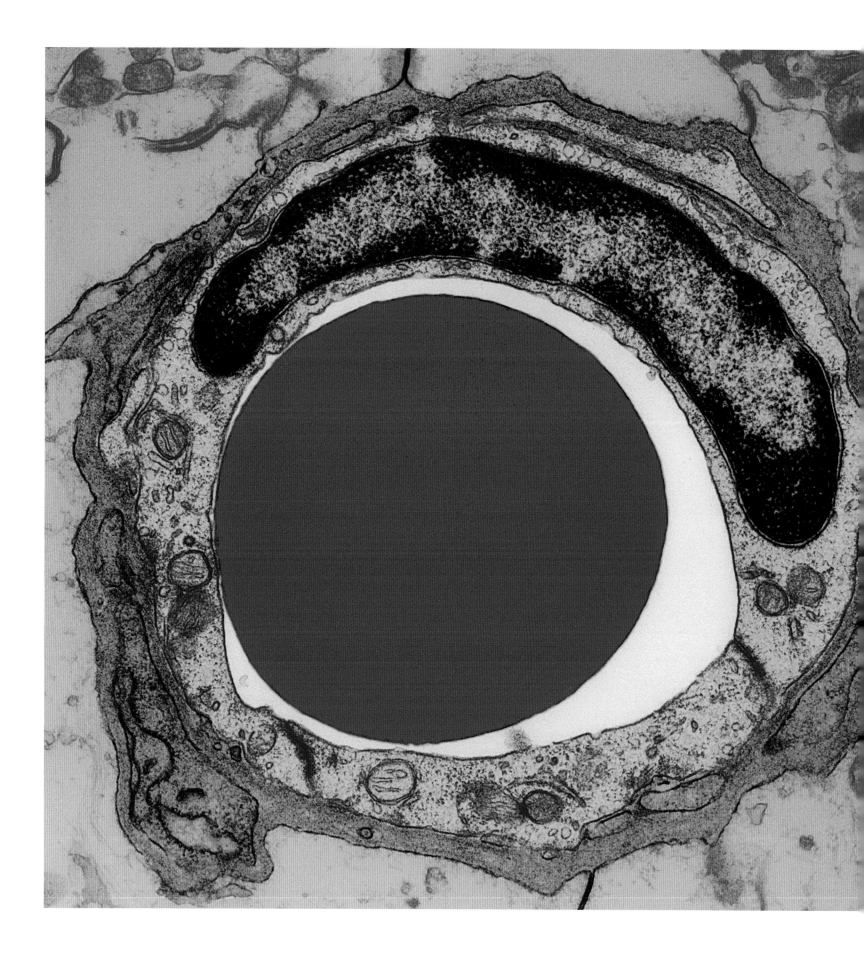

Wir haben sie massenhaft in unserem Körper, und sie geben unserem Blut die Farbe. Wie zerbrechliche Scheiben sehen die roten Blutkörperchen aus, und ihre runde Gestalt kann durch Krankheiten, etwa die Sichelzellenanämie, gefährdet sein. Sie ist nicht nur die am längsten bekannte Blutkrankheit: Bei der Sichelzellenanämie wurde zum ersten Mal erkannt, dass Krankheiten molekulare Ursachen haben können. Nur weil ein einziger Baustein, eine Aminosäure, verändert ist, wechselt der rote Blutfarbstoff Hämoglobin seine Struktur. Er verklumpt und zwingt damit die Blutzellen, die Gestalt einer Sichel anzunehmen, die den Blutfluss erschwert.

Nous en possédons d'énormes quantités et ce sont eux qui donnent au sang sa couleur. Les globules rouges ont l'aspect de disques fragiles, dont la forme arrondie peut être altérée par des maladies du sang. Celle que l'on connaît depuis le plus longtemps est l'anémie à cellules falciformes ou drépanocytose. C'est en étudiant cette forme d'anémie que l'on a compris, pour la première fois, qu'une maladie pouvait avoir une cause moléculaire. Il s'agit, en l'occurrence, d'une anomalie du pigment rouge du sang, l'hémoglobine, dont la structure s'altère, obligeant les globules rouges à prendre une forme de faucille qui entrave leur capacité à circuler dans les vaisseaux capillaires.

Red blood cells are present in huge numbers in our body and are responsible for the colour of our blood. The discoid shape of these fragile-looking cells can be altered by certain blood diseases. The disease first shown to act in this way is sickle cell anemia, which has the additional distinction of being the first disease for which a molecular cause was demonstrated. In sickle cell anemia substitution of a single amino acid alters the structure of hemoglobin, the red blood pigment. The hemoglobin aggregates and in so doing distorts the cell into the shape of a sickle. This hinders blood flow.

Tenemos miles de millones, y a ellos debe la sangre su color. Los glóbulos rojos aparecen al microscopio como frágiles discos; su forma redondeada, de hecho, puede alterarse en diversas enfermedades hematológicas. Una de las más conocidas es la drepanocitosis o anemia de células falciformes, en la que se demostró por primera vez que las enfermedades podían deberse a causas de tipo molecular. La alteración de un solo aminoácido cambia por completo la estructura de la hemoglobina –el pigmento rojo de la sangre–, hace que los glóbulos rojos adopten forma de hoz y dificulta así el flujo sanguíneo.

Human red blood cells. Transmission electron microscopy, copyright Denis Kunkel Microscopy.

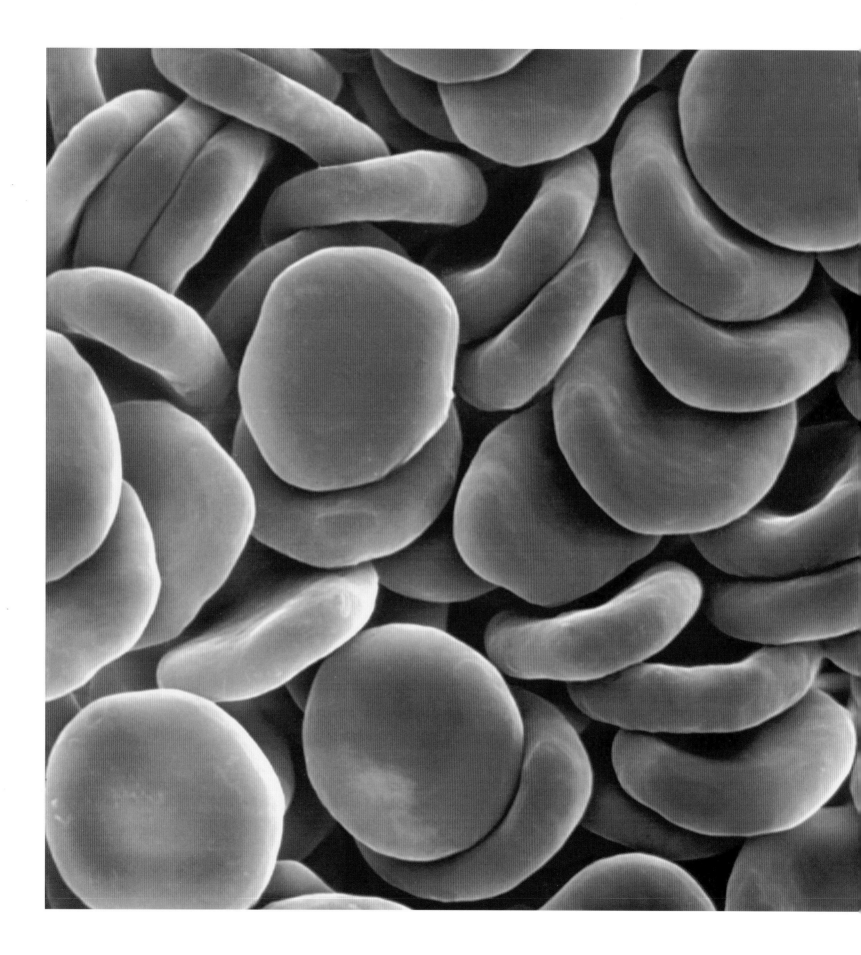

Im Zentrum der Lichtkreise – schöne Artefakte des verwendeten Mikroskops – sieht man ein stachelartiges Gebilde, in dem ein Wissenschaftler einen Kristall erkennt. Wir sehen die gelungene Kristallisation des Proteins Neprilysin, das an der Regulierung des Blutdrucks beteiligt ist. Möglicherweise könnte Bluthochdruck mit Medikamenten behandelt werden, die auf das Neprilysin zielen.

Au centre des halos de lumière, qui proviennent du microscope et ne constituent donc qu'un bel artefact, apparaît une forme hérissée de piquants, en laquelle un œil exercé reconnaît aussitôt un cristal. Ce dernier renferme de la néprilysine, une protéine participant aux mécanismes qui régulent la tension artérielle. Lorsque celle-ci augmente fortement, il est nécessaire de donner des médicaments pour la faire baisser; la néprilysine, dont on peut admirer ici les beaux cristaux, pourrait servir de cible à de tels médicaments.

In the middle of the circles of light, which are produced by the microscope and can thus be regarded as beautiful artefacts, we see a spiny structure that scientists will recognise as a crystal. It is the product of successful crystallisation of a protein known as neprilysin, which plays a part in the regulation of blood pressure. High blood pressure could potentially be treated using drugs that act on neprilysin.

En el centro de los círculos luminosos provocados por el microscopio utilizado, destaca una estructura espinosa que un científico reconocería inmediatamente como un cristal. En él se esconde una proteína llamada neprilisina, que interviene en diversos procesos reguladores de la tensión arterial. En el futuro, los hipertensos podrán tal vez beneficiarse de nuevos medicamentos antihipertensores que actúen sobre la neprilisina.

Crystals of neprilysin, human neutral endopeptidase. Polarising microscopy, Allan D'Arcy, Martine Stihle, Roche Basel.

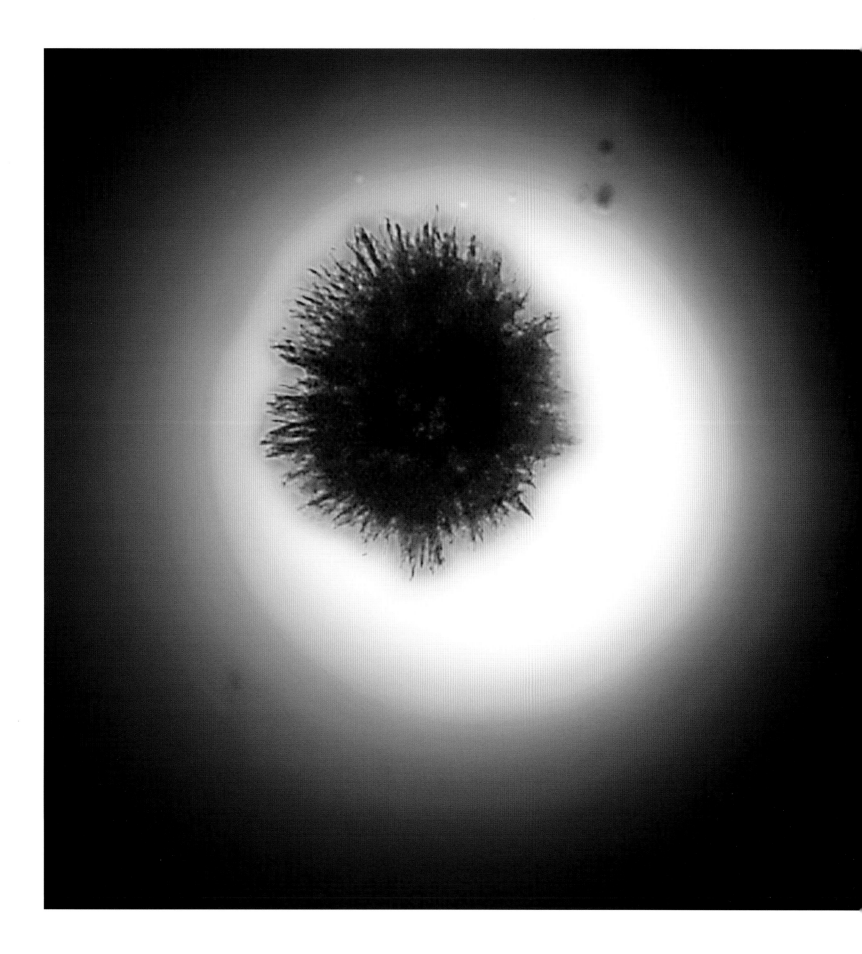

Bringt man Blut auf ein Glasplättchen, dessen Oberfläche so vorbereitet ist, dass sich auf ihm Ablagerungen (Aggregate) bilden und festsetzen können, dann ist es dank der Fluoreszenzmikroskopie möglich, einen Blutpfropfen (Thrombus) in der gezeigten Weise sichtbar zu machen. Die Farben, die vom Rot über das Gelb zum Blau hin variieren, zeigen die zunehmende Größe des Pfropfens an. Das Bild erinnert an Aufnahmen, die wir aus dem Weltall kennen, doch blicken wir nicht in die Tiefe, vielmehr erkennen wir das Höhenprofil des Thrombus.

Lorsqu'on fait couler du sang sur une lamelle de verre dont la surface a été préparée de façon à ce que puissent s'y accrocher et s'y fixer des agrégats sanguins, la microscopie de fluorescence permet de mettre en évidence des formations de sang coagulé, ou thrombus, dont on a ici un exemple. Variant entre le rouge, le jaune et le bleu, les couleurs témoignent de l'importance croissante du thrombus. Cette image fait penser aux photographies prises dans l'espace, sauf qu'il ne s'agit pas ici d'insondables profondeurs, mais du profil d'élévation d'un thrombus.

If blood is allowed to flow over a glass slide whose surface has been prepared in such a way that platelet clumps (aggregates) can form and settle on it in the same way as they do on the walls of blood vessels, the resulting blood clots (thrombi) can be rendered visible by fluorescence microscopy, as in this image. The variation in colour from red through yellow to blue indicates increasing size of the thrombus. The image is reminiscent of pictures of the far reaches of the universe, though what we are seeing here is in fact not a view of depth but a three-dimensional profile of a thrombus.

Si hacemos fluir sangre sobre una placa de vidrio previamente preparada para que se formen en su superficie depósitos o agregados, la microscopia de fluorescencia permite visualizar un trombo o coágulo sanguíneo como en esta imagen. Los colores, que van del rojo al azul pasando por el amarillo, muestran el grosor creciente del trombo. La imagen recuerda a las fotografías del espacio interestelar, pero en esta ocasión no se trata de una imagen de profundidad, sino más bien del relieve o la altura del trombo.

Colour-coded vertical section through a thrombus. Confocal fluorescence microscopy, Remo Hochstrasser, Roche Basel.

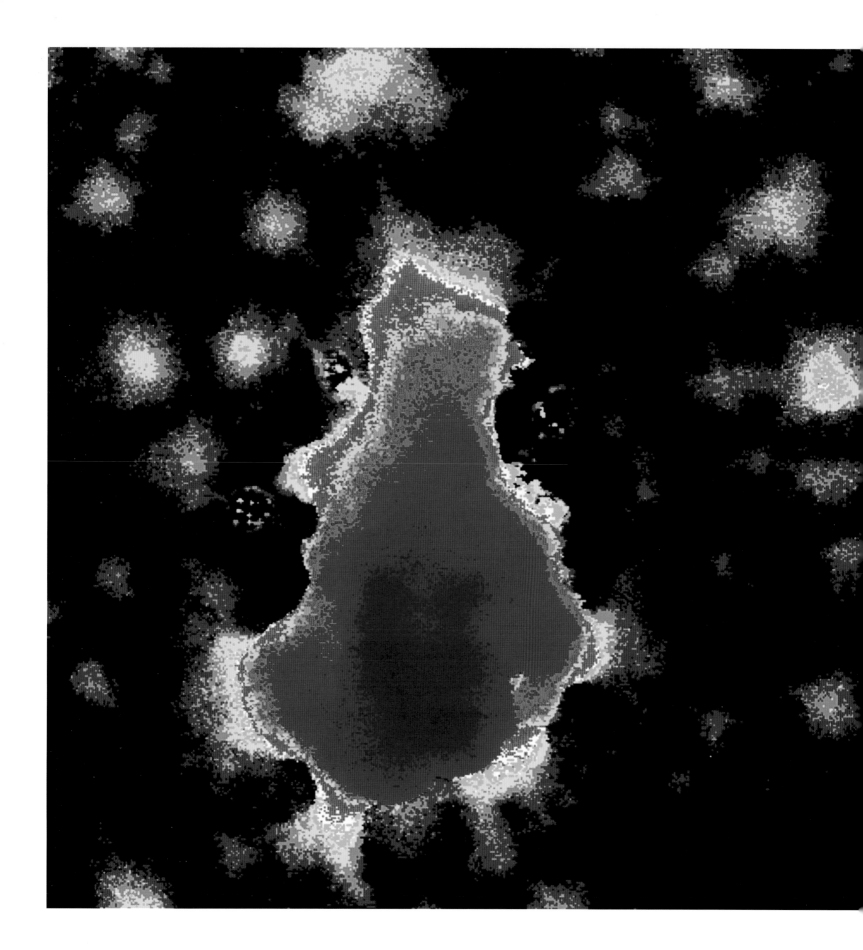

Wir zerlegen die Wirklichkeit gerne, um sie anschließend neu zu ordnen. Unser Möglichkeitssinn schafft dabei zwar ständig neue Wirklichkeiten, aber nur selten wirken sie so schön wie bei diesem komplementären Paar aus zwei Blutkörperchen. Die rote Zelle mit ihrer glatten Oberfläche lässt der weißen Kugel mit ihrer eher zerbrechlich wirkenden Schale den Vortritt. Zusammen mit dem schwarzen Hintergrund vereinigt das Bild die drei Farbtöne, für die es in allen Sprachen der Welt Wörter gibt. Das Bild fasziniert allein schon dadurch, dass wir auf ein Grundmuster des Sehens blicken: Das Rot schiebt sich zwischen die Helligkeit des Tages und die Dunkelheit der Nacht.

Nous aimons décomposer la réalité pour la recomposer différemment. Notre sens du possible crée alors des réalités nouvelles, qui égalent rarement en beauté, il est vrai, la paire complémentaire de cellules sanguines que l'on découvre ici. Le disque rouge, avec sa belle surface lisse, laisse la priorité à la sphère blanche, à l'enveloppe d'apparence plutôt fragile. Avec son fond noir, cette image réunit les trois couleurs pour lesquelles toutes les langues du monde ont inventé des mots. La fascination qui s'en dégage s'explique en partie par le fait que l'on a sous les yeux l'un des motifs fondamentaux de la vision. Le rouge qui se glisse entre la clarté du jour et l'obscurité de la nuit rehausse encore la qualité du spectacle.

We humans love to disassemble reality and then reassemble it according to our imaginations. In so doing, we are constantly constructing new realities, though only rarely are these as beautiful as the complementary pair of blood cells shown here. The smooth-surfaced red cell stands back and lets the white sphere, with its somewhat brittle-looking shell, take the limelight. This image brings together the three universal colours – red, white and the background black – for which all the world's languages have equivalent words. Its allure depends in part on the fact that what we are seeing is a fundamental visual pattern, with the red interposing itself between the brightness of day and the darkness of night.

Nos gusta descomponer la realidad para acto seguido reordenarla de nuevo. Nuestro sentido de la posibilidad crea así constantemente nuevas realidades, pero rara vez tan hermosas como esta pareja complementaria de glóbulos sanguíneos. El glóbulo rojo, de superficie lisa, cede el primer plano al glóbulo blanco con su cobertura de aspecto quebradizo. Con el fondo negro, la imagen reúne los tres tonos cromáticos que conocen sin excepción todas las lenguas del mundo. La fascinación de la imagen obedece, pues, al menos en parte, al hecho de que contemplamos un patrón visual básico. El rojo se intercala entre la claridad del día y la oscuridad de la noche.

Red (erythrocyte) and white (leucocyte) blood cells. Coloured scanning electron microscopy, NIBSC/Science Photo Library.

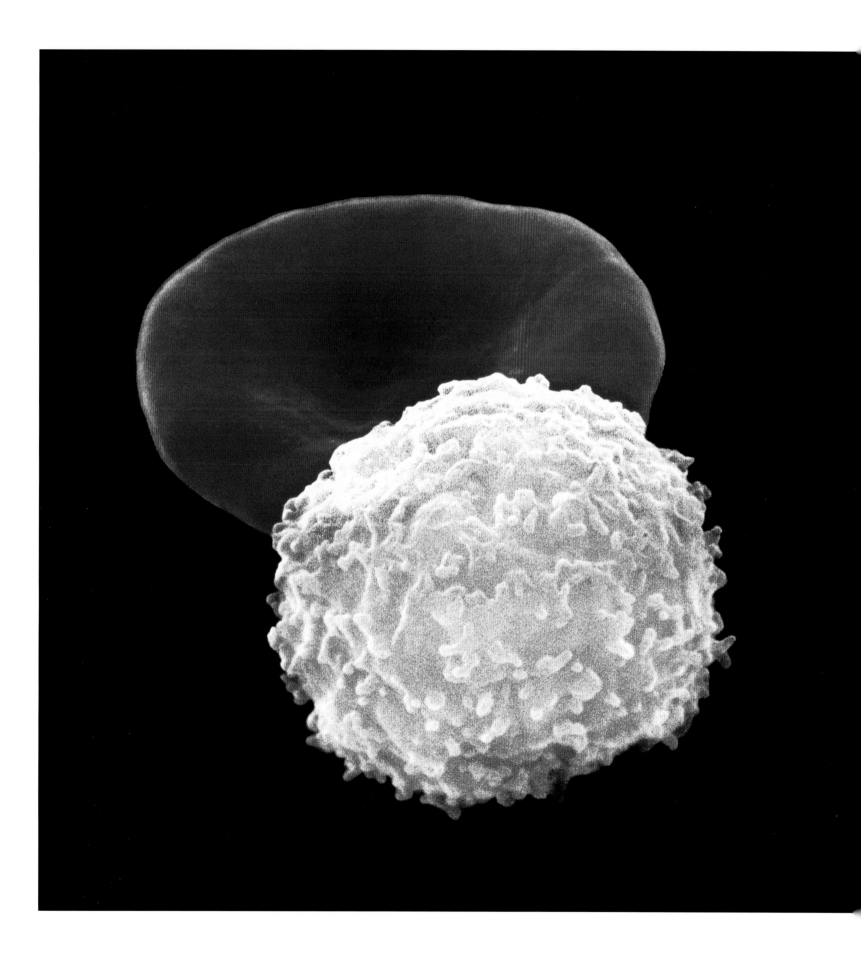

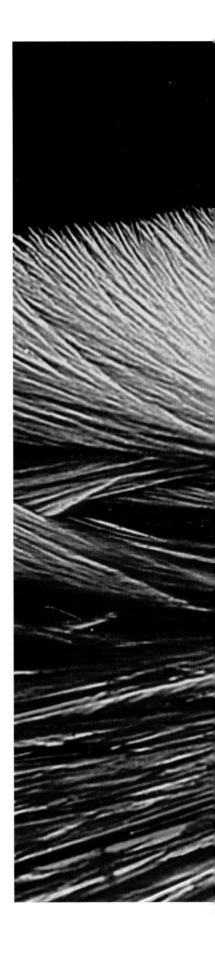

Urogenitalkrankheiten

Stilles Leiden

Les maladies génito-urinaires

Le mal silencieux

Urogenital diseases

Silent suffering

Enfermedades genitourinarias

Padecimientos ocultos

Stilles Leiden

Le mal silencieux

Seit dem 17. Jahrhundert, also seit es eine wissenschaftliche Medizin im modernen Sinne gibt, richten die Menschen ihren diagnostischen Sinn auf die Farbe des Urins. Und von Anfang an haben sie das, was dem Auge zugänglich war und von ihm unterschieden werden konnte, in farbigen Bildtafeln zusammengestellt, die zugleich nützlich und schön waren.

Neben den vielen Krankheiten, die im oftmals hellen Licht der Öffentlichkeit stehen, gibt es zahlreiche Leiden, die von den Betroffenen in aller Stille erduldet werden. Erkrankungen der Harnwege gehören ebenso dazu wie die Leiden an einer Überempfindlichkeit der Blase oder deren zu starke Aktivität bis hin zum völligen Verlust der Kontrolle über dieses Organ. Im letzten Fall ist der operative Eingriff zur Zeit das einzige Mittel, und so stellt sich den Forschern die dringende Aufgabe, Alternativen zu finden. Viele Forschungsaktivitäten konzentrieren sich dabei auf das Gehirn beziehungsweise auf die Frage, über welche Bahnen unser Kopf darüber informiert wird, was sich in der Körpermitte abspielt und wie er die Steuerung in diesem Bereich übernehmen kann.

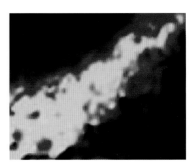

Depuis le XVIIème siècle, où prend corps une médecine scientifique dans l'acception moderne du terme, l'homme exerce son sens diagnostique d'après la coloration des urines. Et il dresse de ce qui est accessible à l'œil et peut être différencié par lui des planches en couleur à la fois utiles et belles.

Si de nombreuses maladies sont exposées à la lumière souvent crue de l'actualité, il en est beaucoup d'autres qui sont endurées en silence. En font partie les maladies des voies urinaires et les affections par irritabilité ou hyperactivité de la vessie, qui peuvent aller jusqu'à l'incontinence, c'est-à-dire jusqu'à la perte de tout contrôle sur cet organe. Sauf la chirurgie, il n'existe pas actuellement de traitement de l'incontinence. Aussi ce domaine suscite-t-il de très nombreuses recherches, dont beaucoup ont pour objet le cerveau ou, plus précisément, les voies nerveuses par lesquelles la tête est informée de ce qui se passe au milieu du corps, ainsi que les mécanismes qui pourraient permettre au cerveau de commander à la vessie.

PP. 60/61: Urea/NaCl/albumin crystal. Polarising microscopy, Andreas Kalbe, Roche Penzberg.

Silent suffering

Padecimientos ocultos

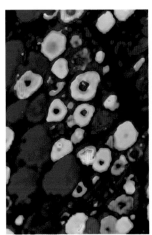

Ever since the birth of modern scientific medicine in the 17th century, humans have looked at the colour of urine in the hope of finding diagnostic clues. In so doing, they have recorded whatever their eyes could see and distinguish in the form of coloured illustrations that are both useful and attractive.

Along with the many diseases that capture public attention, there are others that tend to be endured by their sufferers in complete silence. Among these are urinary tract diseases and irritable bladder syndrome, in which overactivity of the bladder muscle can lead to complete loss of control over urination. As in this eventuality surgery is still the only effective form of treatment, biomedical researchers are under great pressure to find alternatives. Much research activity into this condition is focused on the brain, specifically on the question of what pathways are used to inform the brain of what is going on in the centre of the body, and how the brain can gain control over this type of neural activity.

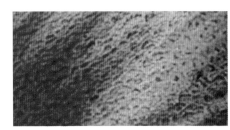

Desde el siglo XVII, en que surge la medicina científica en su acepción moderna, el hombre dirige su sentido diagnóstico al color de la orina. Y desde el comienzo refleja cuanto le es accesible y discernible a través del ojo en láminas coloreadas a un mismo tiempo útiles y bellas.

Junto a muchas enfermedades expuestas ampliamente a la luz pública, existen también muchas otras que se padecen ocultamente y en silencio. Entre ellas se cuentan las enfermedades de las vías urinarias, como las afecciones vesicales que van desde la irritabilidad o la hiperreactividad hasta la incontinencia urinaria. Para esta última no existe en la actualidad más tratamiento que el quirúrgico, de tal modo que este campo supone un reto esencial para los investigadores. Muchas de las investigaciones actuales se concentran en el cerebro y en las vías nerviosas a través de las cuales el cerebro recibe información de cuanto sucede en el resto del cuerpo, así como en los mecanismos neurológicos que intervienen en la regulación de la actividad vesical.

Hier scheint es, als ob ein Vulkan ausbricht und glühende Lava ins Tal sendet. Was so heiß wirkt, sind die Stellen, an denen sich die Farben Grün und Rot überlagern, die in der Lichtmischung zusammen Gelb ergeben. Die einzelnen grünen Punkte zwischen roten und gelben Flächen sieht allerdings nur, wer ganz genau hinschaut. Mit dem Grün gibt sich ein riesiges Protein zu erkennen, das eine Zellhülle, eine Membran, durchspannt und dafür sorgt, dass diese von Ionen durchströmt wird. Die rote Farbe weist darauf hin, dass es sich tatsächlich um Neuronen handelt, die in den Immunofluoreszenzbildern sichtbar werden. Das ganze Geschehen läuft in einem Teil des Nervengewebes ab, das sich in der Umgebung der Blase befindet.

Ne dirait-on pas un volcan en éruption, qui envoie vers la plaine sa lave incandescente? Cette impression d'intense chaleur naît aux endroits où se rencontrent le vert et le rouge, qui donnent le jaune. En y regardant de très près, on discerne, entre les plages de rouge et de jaune, des points verts révélant une protéine géante, traversée par une membrane cellulaire donnant passage à un flux d'ions. Le rouge donne la certitude que les cellules que l'on voit sur cette image en immunofluorescence sont bien des neurones. Le processus se déroule dans une portion du tissu nerveux voisine de la vessie.

We feel we are looking at an erupting volcano discharging glowing lava into a valley. The impression of heat is created at the places where green and red come together to form yellow, though only very close observation reveals the individual green points between the red and yellow areas. The green announces the presence of a giant protein that spans a cell membrane and allows ions to flow through it. In immunofluorescence images such as this, red indicates the presence of neurons. The events seen here are taking place in nerve tissue in the bladder wall.

Ante esta imagen, nos parece contemplar un volcán en erupción que arroja hacia el valle la lava incandescente. Esta ardiente impresión surge de los lugares en los que se funden dos colores, verde y rojo, que juntos forman el amarillo. Sólo fijándonos con atención distinguiremos, entre las superficies rojas y amarillas, algunos puntos verdes aislados, correspondientes a una proteína gigantesca que atraviesa la membrana celular e interviene en el flujo transmembranario de iones. El color rojo confirma que son realmente neuronas lo que vemos en esta microfotografía de inmunofluorescencia. Todo el proceso tiene lugar en una porción de tejido neural próxima a la vejiga urinaria.

Suburothelial nerve plexus of wild type mouse urinary bladder. Fluorescence microscopy, Sanja Novakovic, Roche Palo Alto.

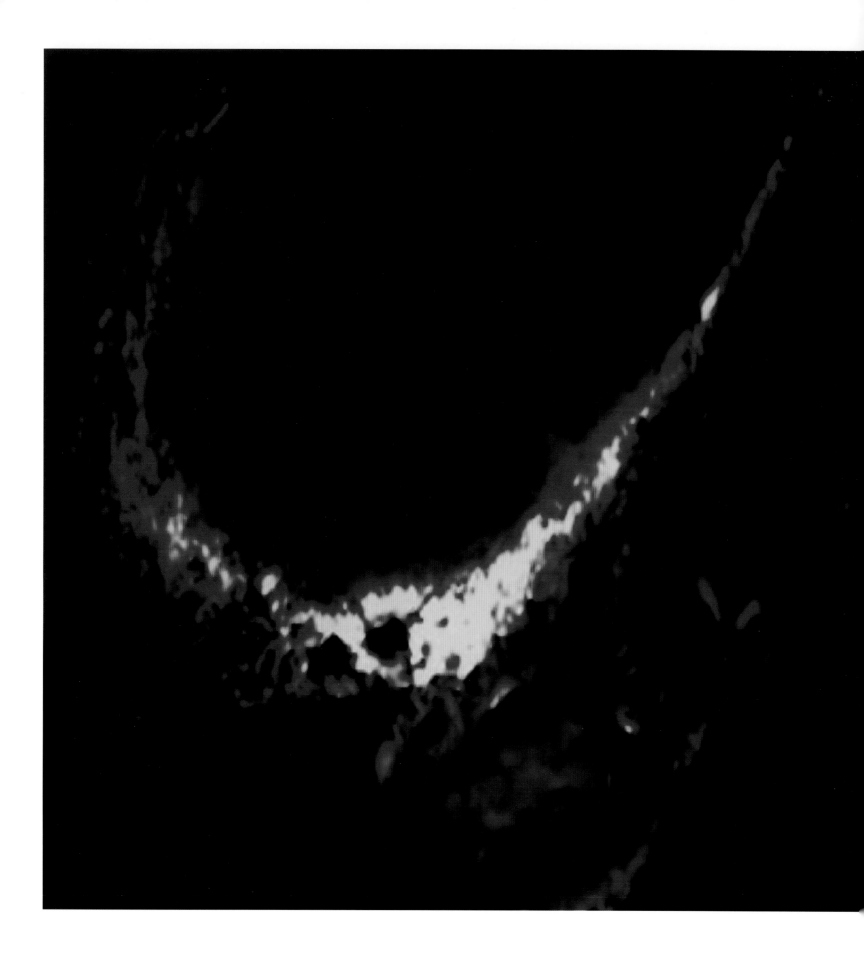

Beim Blick auf das abgebildetete Nervengewebe fallen große und kleine Neuronen auf. Ein quirliges und stechendes Rot, das in vielen kleinen Einheiten sich um komplementär gefärbte und geformte – grüne und große – Strukturen legt. Die roten Färbungen kommen mit Hilfe eines Antikörpers zustande, der dort anbindet, wo ein bestimmter Rezeptor sitzt. Dieser Rezeptor spielt eine entscheidende Rolle bei der Weiterleitung von Informationen aus den Sinneskanälen. Rätselhafte Gebilde, die das Leben steuern und die es zu entschlüsseln gilt, wenn wir leidenden Menschen helfen wollen, ihre Schmerzen zu mildern.

Tissu nerveux où l'œil découvre des neurones de différentes tailles, ainsi qu'une multitude de petites formations, d'un rouge vif et tourbillonnant, entourant de grandes structures teintées en vert, couleur complémentaire du rouge. Le rouge est obtenu grâce à un anticorps qui, après les avoir détectés, se lie à des sites où sont localisés des récepteurs jouant un rôle déterminant dans la transmission des informations arrivées par les canaux sensoriels. Corpuscules remplis de mystères, qui pilotent la vie et qu'il faut déchiffrer si l'on veut aider des personnes qui souffrent à mieux supporter la douleur.

Our gaze falls on nerve tissue containing larger and smaller neurons. Flecks of a vivid and piercing red gather around structures that are complementary to them in both colour (green) and size. The red is produced with the aid of an antibody that locates and binds to a receptor with a central role in the transmission of information coming in via sensory nerves. In order to alleviate pain and help suffering people, we must unravel the mystery of how structures such as these control vital processes.

Corte de tejido nervioso en el que el ojo descubre neuronas grandes y pequeñas. Multitud de pequeñas estructuras de un rojo ardiente rodean a otras estructuras gráficamente complementarias, de color verde y gran tamaño. El color rojo se debe a un anticuerpo capaz de detectar y fijarse a los receptores que intervienen de forma decisiva en la transmisión de las informaciones llegadas a través de las vías sensitivas. Estructuras enigmáticas que gobiernan la vida y que es preciso descifrar si queremos aliviar el dolor de las personas que sufren.

Rat dorsal root ganglion sections (bladder inervation). Fluorescence microscopy, Sanja Novakovic, Roche Palo Alto.

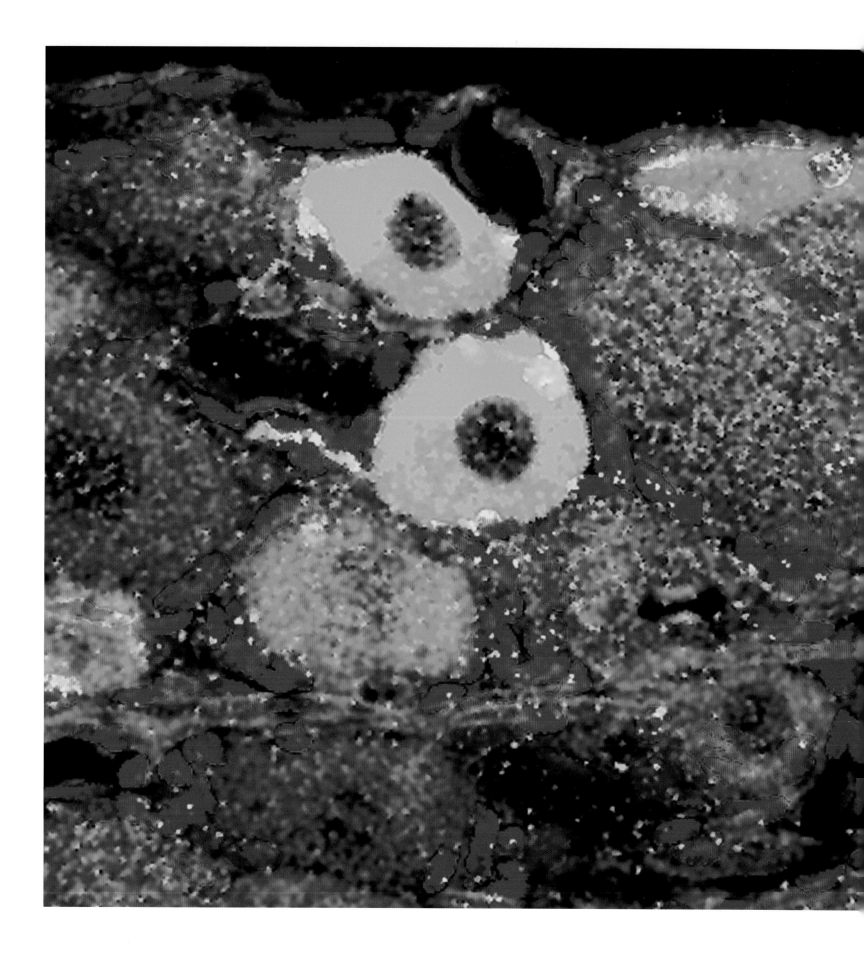

Das komplette Farbspektrum: rot, gelb, grün und blau. Und doch ist es der Farbton am Ende des Spektrums, der in diesem Bild sofort ins Auge fällt, denn Blau macht sich in den Bildern der Wissenschaft relativ rar. Der Farbstoff – «fast-blue dye» – wurde für das hier dargestellte Experiment direkt in die Blase injiziert, von wo es in die sensorischen Neuronen eines Ganglions gelangte. Rot und Grün markieren zwei Rezeptoren, die bei der nervösen Versorgung der Blase eine Rolle spielen. Sie kommen einzeln oder zusammen vor. Letzteres erscheint hier gelb.

Du rouge, du jaune, du vert, du bleu: bref, tout un spectre de couleurs. Relativement rare dans les images que produit la science, le bleu brille ici par sa présence. Utilisé en l'occurrence comme colorant «fast-blue dye», il a été injecté dans une vésicule et transporté sous cette forme vers les neurones sensoriels d'un ganglion. Le rouge et le vert servent de marqueurs pour deux récepteurs intervenant dans l'innervation de la vessie. Ces deux récepteurs sont tantôt séparés, tantôt conjoints. Dans le dernier cas, ils apparaissent en jaune.

Here we see a complete colour spectrum from red through yellow, green and blue. However, it is the blue end of the spectrum that catches the eye. This is because blue makes only rare appearances in scientific images. In the experiment shown here, fast-blue dye has been injected directly into a bladder and from there transported into the sensory neurons of a ganglion. The red and green indicate two receptors that play a role in the nerve supply of the bladder. They can occur individually or together, in which case we see yellow.

Rojo, amarillo, verde, azul: todo el espectro cromático reunido en esta microfotografía. Llama la atención de modo especial el azul, relativamente raro en las imágenes científicas. Utilizado en esta ocasión como colorante «fast-blue dye», se inyectó directamente en una vesícula y fue transportado de esta forma hasta las neuronas sensitivas de un ganglio nervioso. El rojo y el verde actúan como marcadores de sendos receptores que intervienen en la inervación de la vejiga urinaria. Estos dos receptores pueden aparecer por separado o combinados, en cuyo caso lo que vemos es el color amarillo.

Sensory neurons in dorsal root ganglion, responsible for bladder inervation. Fluorescence microscopy, Sanja Novakovic, Roche Palo Alto.

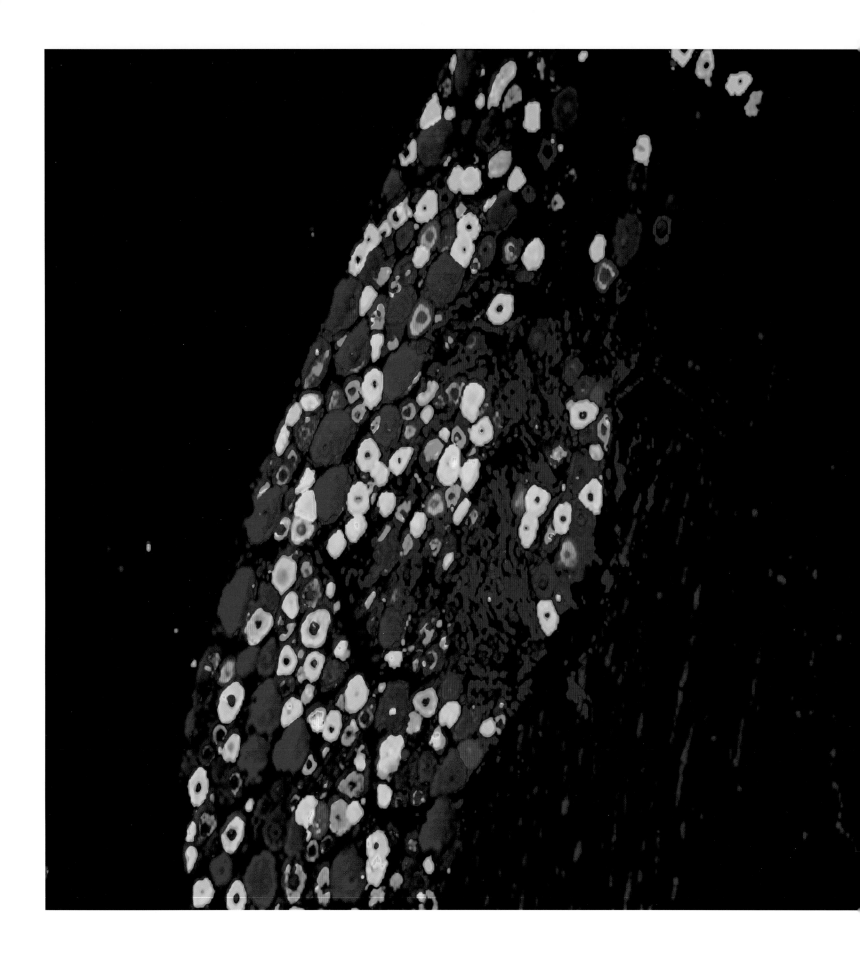

Der schwedische Schriftsteller August Strindberg hat nicht nur Theaterstücke geschrieben, sondern auch versucht, die «verwirrten Sinneseindrücke» zu ordnen, die unser Leben für uns bereithält. Er hat dabei den erstaunlichen Begriff der «natürlichen Kunst» geprägt, bei der ein Künstler wie die launische Natur arbeitet, nämlich ohne festgesetztes Ziel. Diese Mikrofotografie eines Kristalls, der aus einem Harnstoff-Albumin-Gemisch besteht, ist ein wunderbares Beispiel für solche Kunst. Gleichzeitig wirkt die Aufnahme wie eine Illustration des Gedankens, dass Schönheit die Eigenschaft ist, die Dingen Dauer verleiht – auch wenn hinter ihrer Entstehung der Zufall steckt.

L'auteur dramatique et écrivain suédois August Strindberg ne s'est pas contenté d'écrire des pièces de théâtre, il a aussi tenté de démêler les «sensations confuses» que la vie tient en réserve pour l'homme. On lui doit le concept d' «art naturel», où l'artiste, pareil à la capricieuse nature, travaille sans but précis. Ces cristaux d'un mélange d'urée et d'albumine illustrent merveilleusement cet art ainsi que l'observation selon laquelle la beauté, même due au hasard, est la qualité qui donne aux choses de la durée.

As well as writing plays, the Swedish author August Strindberg sought to create order out of the 'deranged sensations' with which life confronts us. In so doing, he coined the striking term 'natural art', in which the artist works like capricious nature, with no firm objective. Microscope images of crystals formed from a mixture of urea and albumin provide a wonderful example of this type of art and at the same time illustrate the concept that beauty is the quality that confers permanency on things – even when it comes about by chance.

El dramaturgo sueco August Strindberg no sólo escribió obras teatrales, sino que intentó también poner orden en las «sensaciones confusas» que la vida depara al ser humano. Fue él quien acuñó el concepto de «arte natural», en el que el artista, a semejanza de la naturaleza caprichosa, trabaja sin un objetivo definido. Estos cristales formados a partir de una mezcla de urea y albúmina constituyen un maravilloso ejemplo de arte natural y, al mismo tiempo, de que la belleza –aun fruto del azar– es la cualidad que convierte en imperecederas a las cosas.

Thiourea crystal. Polarising microscopy, Andreas Kalbe, Roche Penzberg.

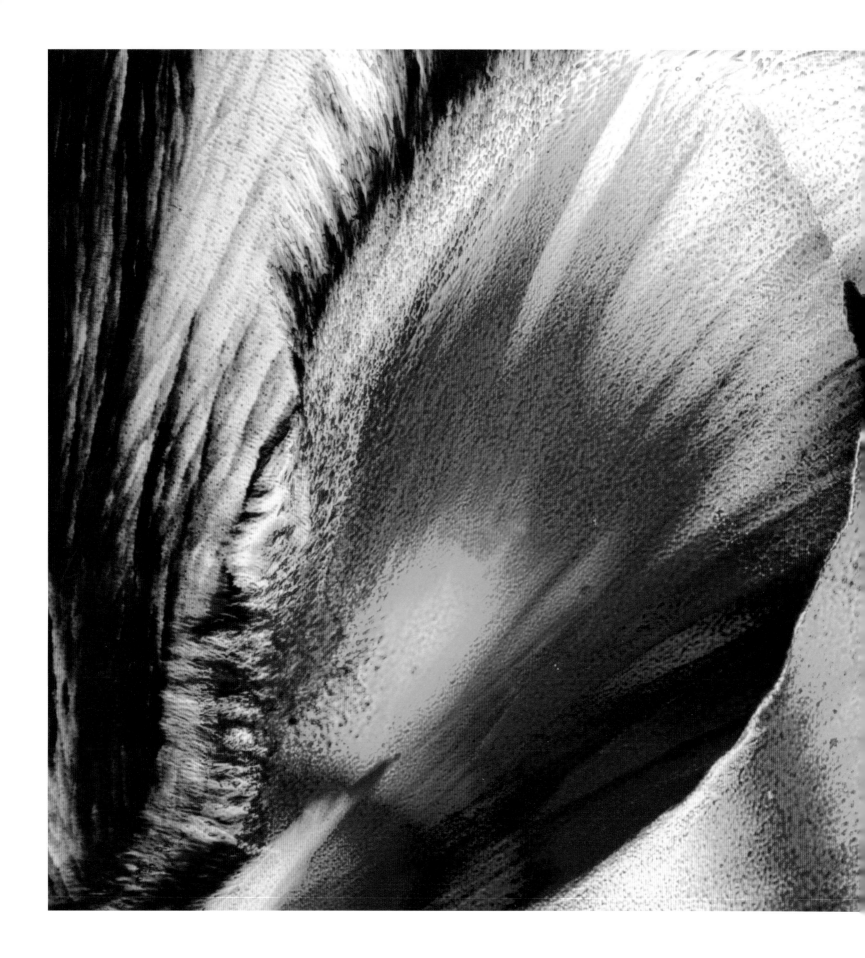

Es mag unglaublich klingen, aber die engen, feinen Verästelungen auf diesem Bild gehören nur zu einer einzigen Nervenzelle. Aus einem deutlich erkennbaren Zellkörper im Zentrum streckt das Neuron seine Fühler in die Umgebung aus – in alle Richtungen und auf allen Wegen. Angesichts dieser dichten Komplexität erscheint der Schulbuchsatz: «Die Zelle ist die Einheit des Lebens», fast banal. Wir erkennen, dass es Einheiten innerhalb dieser Einheit gibt. Die Nervenzelle sieht schon im Kleinen so wie das Netz aus, das sie im Ganzen bildet.

Incroyable mais vrai! Cette image montre à quel point une cellule nerveuse peut être ramifiée. De son corps, parfaitement visible au centre de l'illustration, partent des prolongements qui vont dans toutes les directions et empruntent toutes les voies possibles. Comment ne pas repenser, à la vue de ce spectacle, à la célèbre phrase de nos manuels scolaires: «La cellule est l'unité de la vie.» Et comme elle paraît réductrice par rapport à la réalité que découvre ici le regard, avec cette cellule qui offre déjà l'aspect, à sa toute petite échelle, du réseau dont elle est constitutive.

As extraordinary as it may seem, this image shows the branching structure of a single nerve cell. From the clearly demarcated cell body in the centre of the image, the neuron stretches its feelers out in all directions over a myriad of pathways. Though we can still relate this image to the school-book definition of a cell as 'the basic unit of life', the complexity revealed here makes such a definition seem banal. We see that this unit is made up of subunits and looks like a miniature version of the network formed by neurons throughout the body.

En esta microfotografía se aprecia hasta qué extremos increíbles puede llegar a ramificarse una neurona. De su cuerpo, perfectamente reconocible en el centro de la imagen, se extienden hacia todas partes multitud de prolongaciones. A la vista de este espectáculo, uno recuerda la frase de los libros escolares de biología: «la célula es la unidad esencial de la vida». ¡Y cuán pobre parece en comparación con la realidad que contemplamos! Pues la susodicha unidad aparece integrada por muchas otras unidades, y la neurona, con ser tan pequeña, ofrece todo el aspecto de la red que ella misma conforma.

Cultured neuron. Fluorescence microscopy, Sanja Novakovic, Roche Palo Alto.

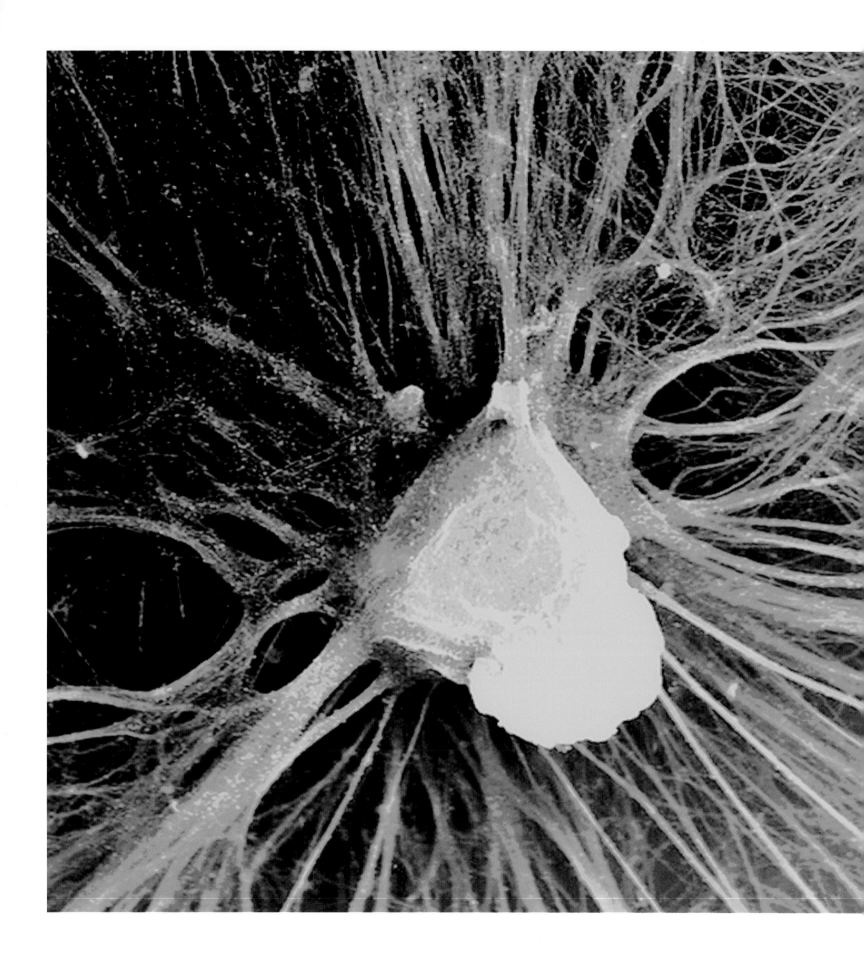

Stoffwechselkrankheiten

Kreisläufe

Les maladies du métabolisme

Cycles de transformation

Metabolic diseases

Cycles

Enfermedades metabólicas

Ciclos

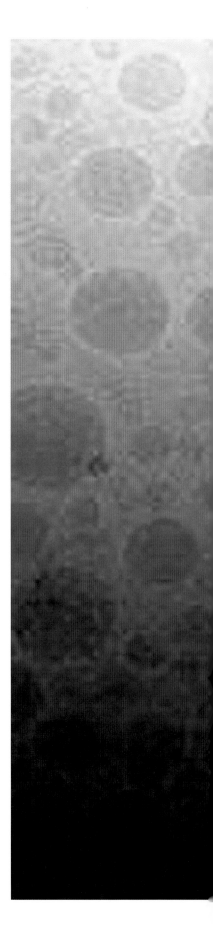

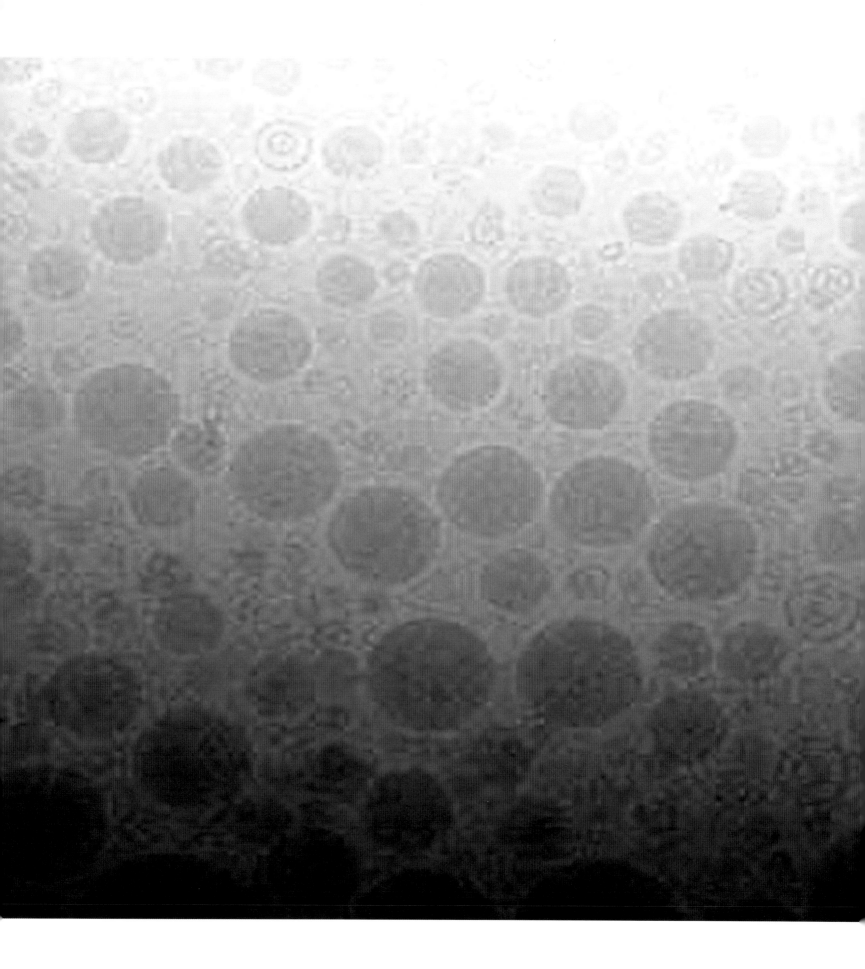

Kreisläufe

Cycles de transformation

Metaphysik, Metamorphose, Metapher – viel sagende Wörter der Wissenschaft, die mit der gleichen griechischen Vorsilbe beginnen. Sie ist seltsam vieldeutig: Nachher, anders, inmitten – all das kann «meta» ausdrücken, also zum einen das, was es nach der Physik zu erkunden gilt; weiterhin das, was sich umgestaltet hat; und schließlich das, was man durch einen bildlichen Ausdruck anderswo hingetragen hat. Beim Metabolismus weist die vielseitige Vorsilbe nach innen. Sie meint den Stoffwechsel und damit die Metamorphose der Moleküle, die dort abläuft, wo kein Auge hinreicht, und die sich unserer Wahrnehmung entzieht.

Es hat lange gedauert, bis die Wissenschaft dem Stoffwechsel konkret auf seine organischen und zellulären Spuren gekommen ist, und noch am Ende der 1960er Jahre gab es viele medizinische Hochschulen und Universitäten, an denen keine Biochemie unterrichtet wurde. Heute überschreiten die Lehrbücher dieses Fachs leicht den Umfang von tausend Seiten, und die Abbildungen darin werden immer raffinierter. Trotzdem bleibt es nach wie vor schwierig, die mit dem Metabolismus verbundenen Formveränderungen und Bewegungen darzustellen. Hier kann es nur um Momentaufnahmen gehen. Auch wenn uns diese Bilder gefallen, ihr Hintergrund bleibt ernst: Eine einzige Stoffwechselkrankheit – Diabetes mellitus – bringt alleine in den USA sechzehn Millionen Menschen in Gefahr – und in jedem Jahr kommt knapp eine weitere Million dazu.

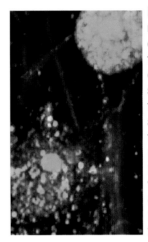

Métaphysique, métamorphose, métaphore, trois termes scientifiques évocateurs, commençant tous trois par le même préfixe grec. «Méta», préfixe aux significations étrangement étendues, peut exprimer la succession, le changement, la participation, c'est-à-dire les questions à explorer après la physique, mais aussi ce qui s'est transformé, enfin, ce que l'on a transposé par une expression imagée. Dans le cas du métabolisme, ce préfixe polyvalent pointe vers l'intérieur, vers les métamorphoses des molécules, qui se produisent où l'œil ne pénètre jamais et qui demeurent soustraites à notre perception.

Il a fallu beaucoup de temps aux scientifiques pour qu'ils comprennent les bases organiques et cellulaires du métabolisme, et il existait encore, fin des années soixante, beaucoup de facultés de médecine et d'universités où la biochimie n'était pas enseignée. Aujourd'hui, les traités de biochimie dépassent allégrement les mille pages, et les illustrations qu'ils contiennent sont de plus en plus raffinées. Il n'en demeure pas moins difficile de représenter les transformations et les processus liés au métabolisme. Il ne peut s'agir que d'instantanés qui, tout en étant plaisants à l'œil, ne doivent pas faire oublier qu'une maladie du métabolisme, le diabète sucré, affecte, à elle seule, seize millions d'Américains, auxquels s'ajoutent, chaque année, presque un million de nouveaux cas.

PP. 74/75: Lipid droplet suspension. Cryotransmission electron microscopy, Bernd Bohrmann, Roche Basel.

Cycles

Ciclos

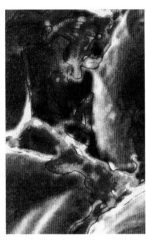

Metaphysics, metamorphosis, metaphor – evocative words that share the same strangely ambiguous Greek prefix. 'Meta' can mean 'after', 'different from' or 'among'. Thus, metaphysics is what remains to be investigated after physics, metamorphosis is a change in shape, and a metaphor is something that has been transported by means of a pictorial expression. In the case of 'metabolism', the versatile prefix refers to internal change, in other words to the constant metamorphosis of molecules that takes place where no eye can see, beyond the limits of our perception.

Only quite recently has any concrete knowledge of the organic and cellular basis of metabolism been acquired, and even in the late 1960s many medical schools and universities did not teach biochemistry. Nowadays, biochemistry textbooks routinely run to over a thousand pages, and the illustrations they contain are becoming ever more elaborate. Nevertheless, the movements and changes in shape associated with metabolic processes remain difficult to represent. Illustrations of these processes can be no more than snapshots, and, as appealing as we may find them, we must not lose sight of the fact that a single metabolic disease – diabetes mellitus – afflicts sixteen million people in the USA alone, and that this figure is increasing by a million each year.

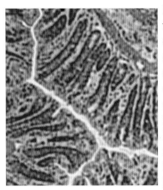

Metafísica, metamorfosis, metáfora: tres tecnicismos evocadores que comparten un mismo prefijo griego, extrañamente polisémico. «Meta-», en efecto, puede significar «después», «distinto» o «entre». Así, la metafísica es lo que está más allá de la física; la metamorfosis, un cambio de forma, y la metáfora, el uso de las palabras con un nuevo sentido descubierto por la imaginación. En el caso de «metabolismo», este polisémico prefijo griego hace referencia a los cambios moleculares que se realizan en la materia viva, donde el ojo no llega, más allá de los límites de nuestra percepción.

Pasó mucho tiempo antes de que los científicos adquirieran conocimientos concretos sobre las bases celulares y orgánicas del metabolismo, y todavía hacia 1970 había muchas facultades de medicina en las que no se enseñaba la bioquímica. En la actualidad, los tratados de bioquímica sobrepasan con facilidad el millar de páginas, y sus ilustraciones son cada vez más refinadas. A pesar de ello, sigue siendo muy difícil representar los movimientos y los cambios morfológicos asociados a los procesos metabólicos. Se trata únicamente de meras instantáneas, que, por atractivas que nos resulten, no deberían hacernos olvidar que una sola enfermedad metabólica, la diabetes sacarina, afecta a 16 millones de personas sólo en los Estados Unidos, a los cuales se suma otro millón de diabéticos cada año.

Stoffwechselkrankheiten, die unerkannt bleiben, wirken sich oftmals im Nervensystem aus, und zu den zahlreichen Aufgaben der medizinischen Forschung gehört es, Verfahren zu finden, mit denen sich neurotoxische Wirkungen nachweisen lassen. Ein gangbarer Weg ist die Untersuchung der Isolierschicht, die unsere Neuronen von Natur aus haben und die ihre Qualität verbessert. Sie setzt sich aus einem Stoff namens Myelin zusammen – auf dem Bild als markante rote Ringe zu erkennen. Das hervorstechende Rot des hier gezeigten peripheren Beinnervs kommt nicht allein durch Färbemethoden zustande, sondern zusätzlich durch die Bildbearbeitung am Computer. So wird die Aufnahme nicht nur schöner, sondern auch präziser.

Non diagnostiquées, les maladies du métabolisme s'expriment souvent au niveau du système nerveux central. Il appartient donc aux spécialistes de la recherche médicale de trouver des procédés permettant de repérer les phénomènes neurotoxiques dus à ces maladies. L'une des méthodes qu'ils ont inventées consiste à examiner la gaine de myéline qui entoure les neurones. Les anneaux rouges que l'on voit sur l'image donnent une idée de la structure de ces couches de myéline. Il s'agit, en l'occurrence, d'un nerf périphérique de la jambe, dont la belle couleur rouge n'est pas uniquement un effet de coloration mais provient aussi du procédé de traitement de l'image utilisé par l'ordinateur. Le résultat n'en est que plus beau et plus précis.

Metabolic diseases that remain undiagnosed often affect the nervous system, and one of the many tasks facing medical research is to find ways of identifying neurotoxic effects. One approach to this problem is to study the natural, highly efficient insulating layer that surrounds our neurons. It is composed of a material known as myelin, shown in this image as striking red rings. In the peripheral nerve shown here, the eye-catching colour is produced not just by staining techniques, but also by computer image analysis. This improves both the appearance and the clarity of the images.

Buena parte de las enfermedades metabólicas aún desconocidas afectan al sistema nervioso. Entre las múltiples tareas de la investigación médica actual, pues, destaca la necesidad de descubrir el modo de identificar los efectos neurotóxicos. Una forma de abordar esta cuestión consiste en investigar la capa de mielina que rodea a las neuronas, que en la imagen aparece como un anillo rojo. Las fibras nerviosas de la pierna aquí representadas toman este color rojo tan llamativo no sólo merced a los colorantes utilizados, sino también al tratamiento gráfico posterior con ayuda del ordenador. De esta forma las imágenes ganan tanto en belleza como en precisión.

Peripheral nerve in the leg, showing multiple cross-sections of individual nerves. Light microscopy and image analysis, Bonnie Lockard, Roche Nutley.

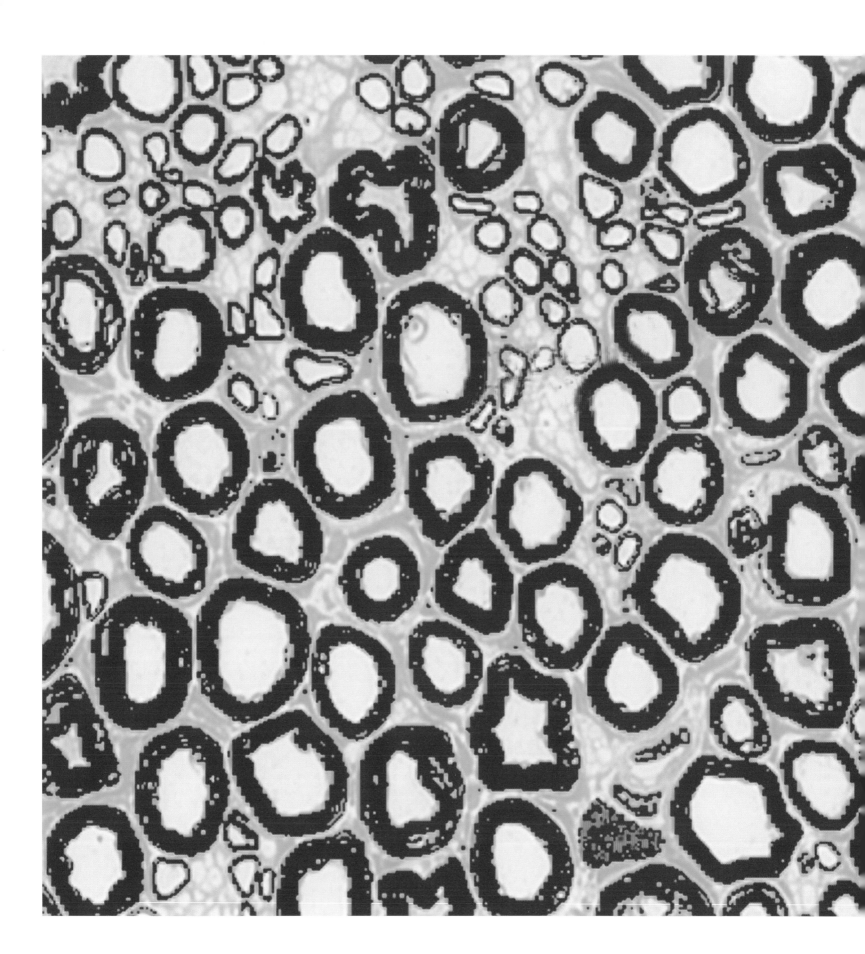

Durchsichtig wie Glasscheiben erscheinen die verschieden großen Flächen, die regelmäßig und unregelmäßig zugleich sind. Der inneren Ordnung der Kristalle entspricht keine äußere Festlegung – weder in der Form noch in der Größe. Das Farbenspiel erhöht den Reiz für den Betrachter. In der Mitte all der Formen und Farben steckt ein Molekül, das in allen Geweben vorkommt und große Popularität genießt – das Cholesterin.

Des surfaces de grandeur variable, à la fois régulières et irrégulières, transparentes comme des plaques de verre. L'ordre qui règne à l'intérieur des cristaux n'a pas, qu'il s'agisse de la forme ou de la taille, de pendant extérieur. Ravi par le jeu des couleurs, le spectateur l'est aussi d'apprendre qu'il y a, au milieu de ces formes et de ces couleurs, une molécule présente dans tous les tissus de l'organisme et dont on parle beaucoup: le cholestérol.

The variously sized regular and irregular surfaces seen here seem as transparent as panes of glass. The internal order of the crystals is not matched by any external regularity of shape or size. The charm of the image is increased by the kaleidoscopic colours and by the knowledge that at the centre of these different forms and hues is a molecule with a high public profile that is found in all tissues – cholesterol.

Transparentes como pedazos de vidrio parecen estas superficies de formas y tamaños diversos. El orden interno de los cristales no se corresponde con ninguna regularidad externa de forma o tamaño. El encanto que la imagen ejerce sobre el observador se acentúa por el juego de colores y el hecho de que en el origen de todas estas formas se halla una molécula presente en todos los tejidos y de lo más famoso: el colesterol.

Cholesterol crystals. Polarisation microscopy, Wellcome Photo Library.

Jeder, der sich bei diesem Bild primär auf die Formwahrnehmung konzentriert, wird Gefallen an dem großen runden Außenkreis finden. Diesem entspricht ein weißer Ring in der Mitte, von dem ein ganzes System von immer feineren Verzweigungen ausgeht. Dazwischen befindet sich ein Gebilde, das an eine stehende Welle, ein physikalisches Phänomen, erinnert. Im Inneren des Körpers, genauer im Darm, finden sich diese Formen – Kreise und Wellen –, die wir mit Hilfe des Mikroskops sichtbar machen können.

L'œil qui ne s'attache qu'aux formes visibles sera tout de suite séduit par le grand anneau extérieur, auquel fait pendant le cercle blanc du centre, dont partent des arborescences qu'enveloppe une formation faisant penser à une vague figée, qu'évoquent souvent les physiciens. Ces cercles et ces ondes, que l'on découvre grâce au microscope, se trouvent dans l'intestin grêle d'un rat.

Anybody whose eyes are drawn towards shapes will be attracted immediately by the large outer ring and the small white disc in the centre of this image. The system of branches radiating out from the disc is enclosed within a structure reminiscent of what physicists refer to as a standing wave. The circles, waves and other forms rendered visible here by the microscope are found in the intestine.

En esta imagen llaman la atención de entrada el gran círculo exterior y el pequeño círculo blanco central. De este último parten unas ramificaciones incluidas en una estructura que recuerda a lo que los físicos llaman una onda estacionaria. El microscopio nos ofrece la posibilidad de descubrir estas formas –círculos y ondas– en el interior del cuerpo, más exactamente en el intestino delgado.

Section through the small intestine of a rat; transmitted light microscopy after histological staining. Bernd Bohrmann, Claudia Richardson, Roche Basel.

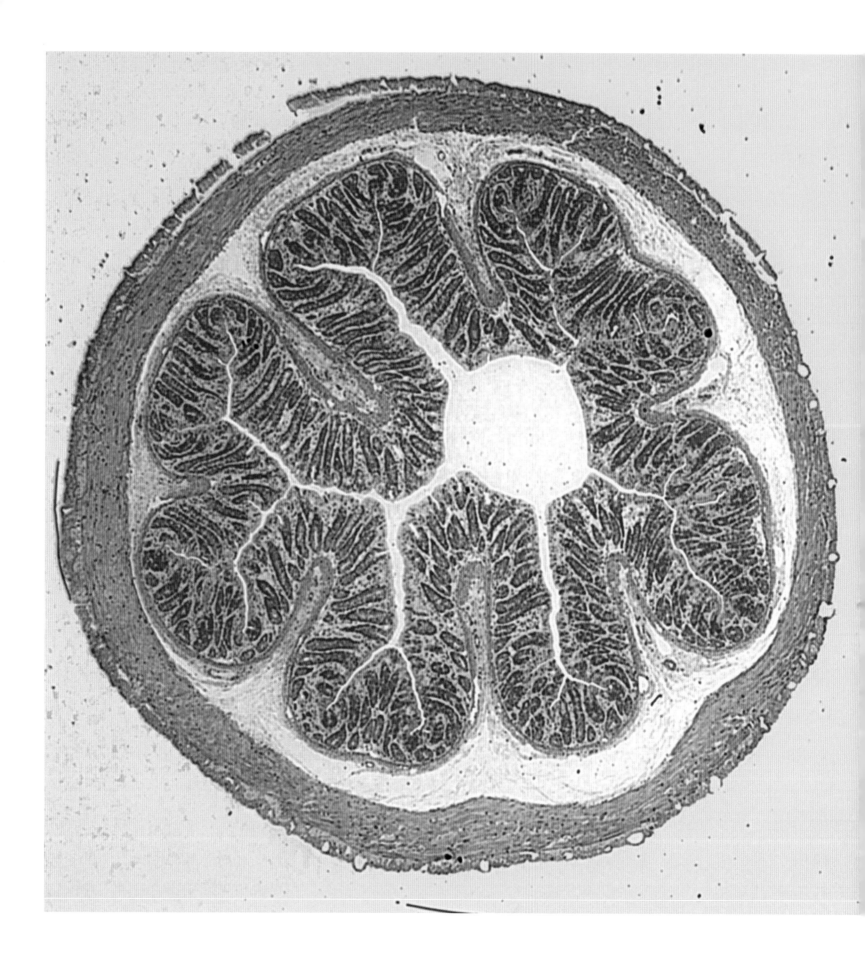

Was so wohlgeformt und reichhaltig aussieht, sind Fettzellen. Dass sie so dicht gepackt erscheinen wie Pralinen in einer Schachtel, ist vielleicht kein Zufall. Die Zellen zeigen ihren Glanz, und sie machen deutlich, wie weich sie sind. Es ist erstaunlich, wie die Form im Kleinen vorgibt, was schließlich äußere Gestalt wird. Hierbei wird auf plastische Weise eine uralte Gedankenbrücke der Menschen anschaulich, die gerne nach Entsprechungen und Korrespondenzen suchen, um den Weg aus der vertrauten in die verborgene Welt zu finden.

Ces éléments aux formes rebondies sont des cellules spécialisées dans le stockage des graisses (adipocytes). Ainsi tassées les unes contre les autres, on dirait des chocolats dans une boîte, et ce n'est peut-être pas un hasard. Elles ont le brillant qui leur sied et l'on devine tout de suite leur onctuosité. Il est étonnant de constater à quel point elles préfigurent, à leur minuscule échelle, l'apparence extérieure du corps. Cela n'illustre-t-il pas de façon très palpable une tendance vieille comme l'humanité à chercher des analogies et des correspondances pour passer plus facilement du monde familier au monde caché.

The abundant, well-formed structures seen here are fat cells. The fact that they appear as tightly packed as chocolates in a box may be more than fortuitous. We see the sheen and softness that these cells actually have. It is extraordinary how this depiction in miniature seems to mirror the corresponding body's outer form. This is a vivid illustration of a primordial human tendency: we look for associations and parallels as we make our way from the familiar to the hidden.

Esto que aquí vemos son adipocitos o células grasas. El hecho de que aparezcan tan apretadas como unos bombones en su caja, no obedece, quizás, al azar. Se aprecia también claramente el brillo y la untuosidad propios de los adipocitos. Resulta asombroso cómo estas células revelan, en su escala diminuta, el auténtico aspecto exterior. Ello ilustra de forma plástica una tendencia primordial de los seres humanos: nuestra tendencia a buscar asociaciones y paralelismos para hallar la senda que nos conduzca de lo familiar a lo oculto.

Coloured adipocytes (fat cells) that form adipose connective tissue. Scanning electron microscopy, QUEST/Science Photo Library.

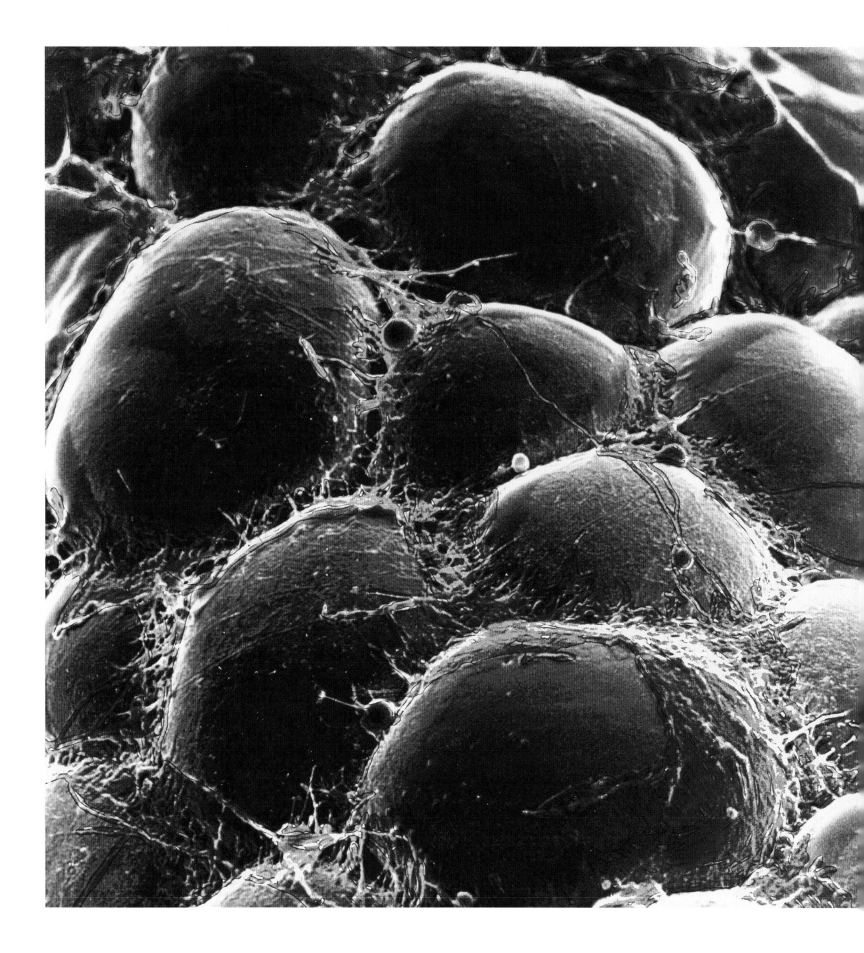

Die leuchtend grünen Punkte vor dem rot-blauen Hintergrund kennzeichnen die Stellen im Gehirn (Rezeptoren), von denen aus ein Hormon namens Orexin seine Wirkung entfaltet. Die Forscher verstehen Hormone als Signale, deren Botschaft mit Hilfe von Rezeptoren empfangen und weitergeleitet wird. Die Aufgabe der Rezeptoren kann vielfältig sein. Wenn sie besetzt sind, empfinden wir Hunger oder Müdigkeit. Wie eng beide zusammenhängen, weiß jeder, der sein Mittagschläfchen schätzt.

Se détachant sur fond rouge et bleu, les points d'un vert lumineux que l'on découvre sur cette image montrent la répartition, dans le cerveau (récepteurs), des sites à partir desquels une hormone, l'orexine, déploie ses effets. Pour les scientifiques, les hormones sont des signaux dont le message est reçu et retransmis à l'aide de récepteurs. Les tâches des récepteurs peuvent être très diverses. Lorsqu'ils sont occupés, l'individu éprouve un besoin de nourriture ou de sommeil. Tout amateur de sieste sait combien ces deux sensations peuvent être voisines.

The bright green spots on a red-blue background indicate the sites of action in the brain (receptors) of a hormone known as orexin. Scientists see hormones as bearers of messages that are received and passed on by receptors. The receptors have a number of functions. When they are occupied, the person feels a need to eat or sleep. Those of us who like taking an afternoon nap know just how closely these two physiological functions are related.

Los puntos verdes brillantes que destacan sobre el fondo rojiazul corresponden a los lugares del cerebro (receptores) en los que ejerce su acción una hormona llamada orexina. Para los investigadores, las hormonas son señales o mediadores cuyo mensaje se recibe y se transmite a través de receptores. Los receptores desempeñan funciones muy diversas. Cuando están ocupados, la persona siente ganas de comer y de dormir. Cuán estrechamente relacionadas se hallan estas dos sensaciones lo saben bien quienes gustan de echar una cabezadita después de comer.

Orexin, a protein thought to be involved in the control of eating and sleeping. Confocal microscopy, Chris Guérin & Knoll Ltd/Wellcome Photo Library.

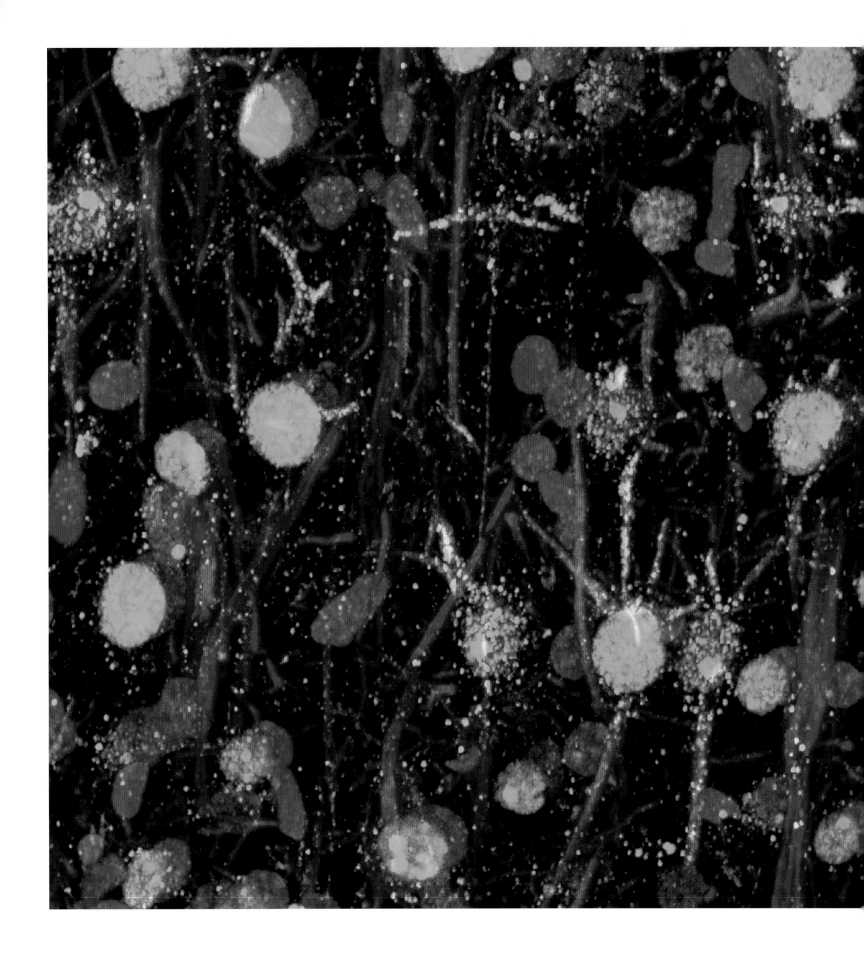

Wenn man Fetttröpfchen direkt im Lichtmikroskop betrachtet, sehen sie aus wie Regentropfen auf Autolack. Die im Bild sichtbaren Kügelchen kann man im Zwölffingerdarm eines Menschen finden, der versucht, etwas gegen seine Fettleibigkeit zu tun und einen Lipasehemmer eingenommen hat. Der fast tausendfach vergrößerte Blick auf das Geschehen im Körper hilft den Wissenschaftlern und Ärzten, den Wirkmechanismus besser einzuschätzen.

Ce que l'on voit ici ne sont pas des gouttes de pluie sur la carrosserie d'une automobile, mais des gouttelettes de graisse telles qu'elles apparaissent au microscope photonique. Ces jolies sphères bleues se trouvent telles quelles dans le duodénum d'une personne qui a entrepris de lutter contre son obésité en prenant un inhibiteur de la lipase. Le fait de voir, sous grossissement de près de mille fois, ce qui se produit dans l'organisme permet aux scientifiques et aux médecins d'évaluer avec précision le mécanisme d'action du médicament.

If fat droplets are observed directly under a light microscope, they take on the appearance of raindrops on the surface of a car. The little globules seen in this image are present in the duodenum of a person who is doing something about his obesity by taking a lipase inhibitor. This view of the internal workings of the body, taken at a magnification of almost a thousand, helps doctors and scientists elucidate the mechanism of action of this type of drug.

Si uno contempla las gotículas de grasa directamente con el microscopio electrónico, parecen talmente gotitas de lluvia sobre el capó de un automóvil. Las burbujas azules que vemos en la fotografía existen tal cual en el duodeno de una persona obesa que toma un inhibidor de la lipasa para intentar adelgazar. La posibilidad de contemplar, aumentado un millar de veces, lo que sucede en el interior del organismo, permite a los científicos y a los médicos esclarecer el mecanismo de acción de este tipo de medicamentos.

Lipid droplet suspension from a human duodenum. Light microscopy with interference contrast, Bernd Bohrmann, Bruno Wessner, Roche Basel.

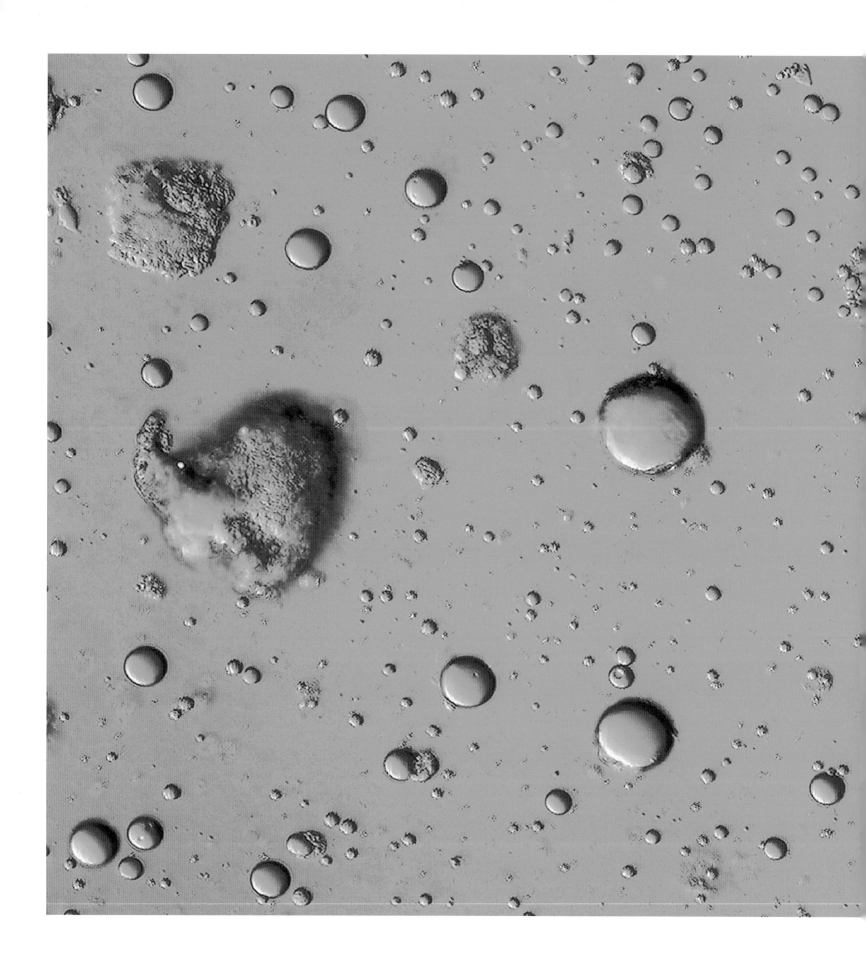

Elegante Formen in warmen Farbtönen. Zwar werden sie von links oben nach rechts unten immer kleiner, die Grundfigur, die den Rahmen des Geschehens vorgibt, bleibt aber stets intakt. Dargestellt wird eine Zeitserie, die zeigt, wie der Inhalt eines Magens mehr und mehr abnimmt. Die verspeiste Mahlzeit war mit dem Stoff versetzt, den Forscher als Tetrahydrolipstatin bezeichnen. Das Faszinierende an dieser Bildfolge ist, dass sich unsere Wahrnehmung sofort auf das bei allem Wandel Unveränderte konzentriert. Eine Herausforderung an unsere Sinne.

On croirait un tissu imprimé aux chauds coloris, dont les motifs, tout en devenant de plus en plus petits, conservent rigoureusement leur forme de base. Il s'agit, en fait, d'un estomac photographié à divers moment de sa vidange. Au bol alimentaire a été ajoutée de la tétrahydrolipstatine. Bien que ce qui intéresse ici le scientifique soit le changement, le regard s'attache immédiatement à la conservation de la forme et c'est ce qui, en tenant les sens en éveil, fait la fascination de cette série d'images.

Elegant patterns in bright, warm colours. Although the size of the object diminishes from top left to bottom right, the basic shape depicted in these images remains intact and recognisable throughout. This series shows how the content of the stomach diminishes over time. The meal consumed by this person contained a substance known as tetrahydrolipstatin. The fascinating thing about these images is that we immediately recognise the constant amidst all the change confronting our perceptions.

Elegante distribución de figuras de cálidos colores. Aunque las figuras disminuyen de tamaño desde el ángulo superior izquierdo hasta el ángulo inferior derecho, la forma básica permanece inalterada y plenamente reconocible a lo largo de toda la serie. Esta serie de imágenes muestra cómo disminuye con el tiempo el contenido gástrico. La comida ingerida por esta persona contenía un medicamento llamado orlistat. Lo fascinante de esta serie gammagráfica es cómo somos capaces de reconocer de inmediato, de entre todo lo cambiante, aquello que permanece constante. Un verdadero desafío para nuestros sentidos.

Distribution of tetrahydrolipstatin in chyme; time series of stomach emptying. Scintigraphy, Remo Hochstrasser, Hans Lengsfeld, Roche Basel; Daniel Matzinger, Cantonal Hospital, Basel.

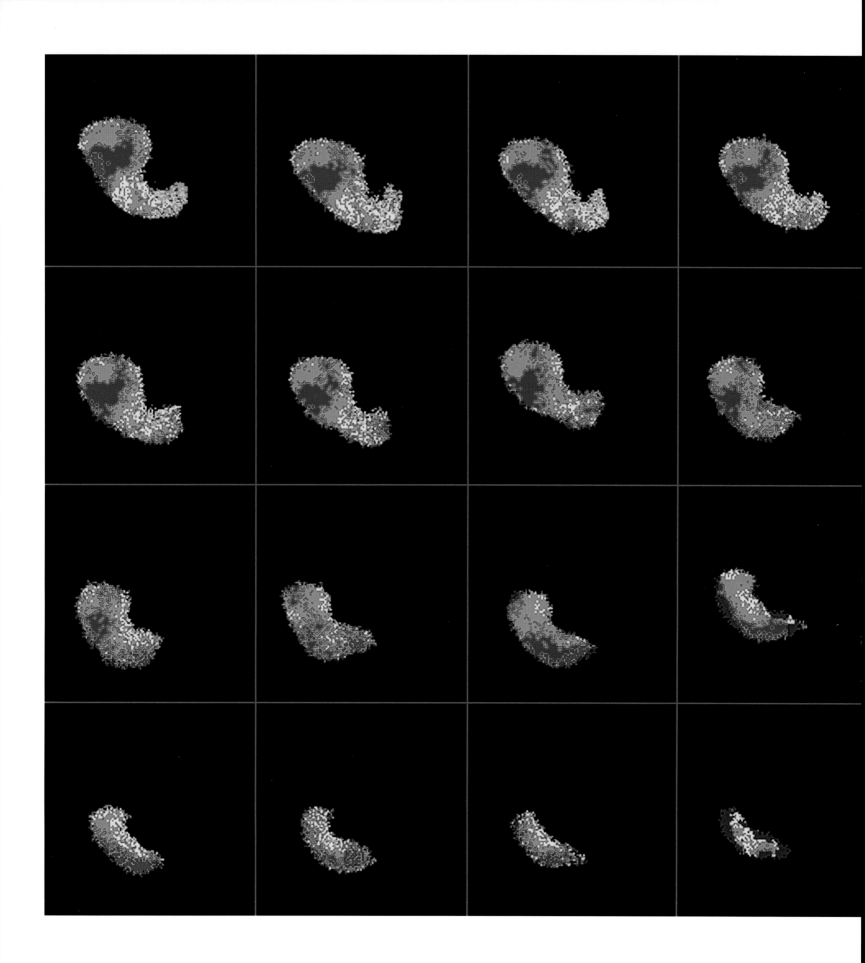

Hinter diesem Bild verbergen sich neue Techniken und viele Hoffnungen. Was wie ein Sternenhimmel aussieht und auch so bunt wie die Nacht ist, wenn nicht die Augen, sondern physikalische Geräte zum Himmel gerichtet sind, stellt in Wirklichkeit einen DNA-Chip dar. Auf seiner Oberfläche können viele tausend Gentests auf einmal durchgeführt werden. Jedes Pünktchen markiert ein Testergebnis, und die unterschiedlichen Farben sagen dem Fachmann, welche Gene aktiv sind. Man hofft, eines Tages die geeigneten Testkombinationen zu finden, mit denen es möglich ist, in den Chips eindeutige Muster zu identifizieren – ganz ähnlich, wie wir es vom Himmel mit seinen Sternzeichen kennen. Damit könnte eine «Genomologie» entstehen, die für das Genom ermöglicht, was die Kosmologie für den Kosmos ermöglicht hat – nämlich seine Geschichte zu ergründen.

Derrière cette image se cachent des techniques nouvelles et de grands espoirs. Ce qui apparaît comme un ciel étoilé et resplendit de toutes les couleurs de la nuit lorsqu'on braque vers le ciel non pas son propre regard, mais celui d'instruments de physique, est en réalité une micromatrice multigénique, c'est-à-dire une surface permettant de faire plusieurs milliers de tests génétiques à la fois. Chaque point représente un résultat, dont la couleur indique au spécialiste quelles sont les gènes impliqués. L'espoir est de parvenir un jour à des combinaisons de tests permettant de faire apparaître des motifs semblables aux signes astrologiques que l'on voit dans le ciel. Cela pourrait donner naissance à une «génomologie» permettant pour le génome ce que la cosmologie a permis pour le cosmos, c'est-à-dire d'en comprendre la formation et l'évolution.

This image is the product of new techniques that have inspired much hope. What looks like a confusion of stars in the night sky, viewed through a telescope, is in fact a DNA chip – a surface on which many thousands of genetic tests can be performed simultaneously. Each spot indicates a test result, and the different colours tell the expert which genes are active. It is hoped that one day DNA chip test combinations will be found that produce patterns that are as readily identifiable as the different constellations in the night sky. This could give rise to a discipline of 'genomology', which could do for the genome what cosmology has done for the cosmos, namely probe its origins.

Tras esta imagen se ocultan nuevas técnicas y grandes esperanzas. Esto que parece un firmamento estrellado contemplado a través de un telescopio, es en realidad una micromatriz multigénica, que permite realizar de forma simultánea millares de análisis genéticos. Cada uno de los puntitos, cada una de las estrellas, corresponde a un resultado analítico, cuyo color indica al especialista cuáles son los genes activos. La esperanza radica en la posibilidad de descubrir algún día las combinaciones analíticas adecuadas para reconocer en estas matrices multigénicas patrones semejantes a las constelaciones que identificamos en la bóveda celeste. Ello abriría las puertas a una nueva ciencia, la «genomología», capaz de conseguir para el genoma lo que la cosmología para el cosmos: esclarecer su historia.

DNA chip analysis of a cell culture sample from patients with Tangier disease. Michael Pech, Uwe Hobohm, Roche Basel.

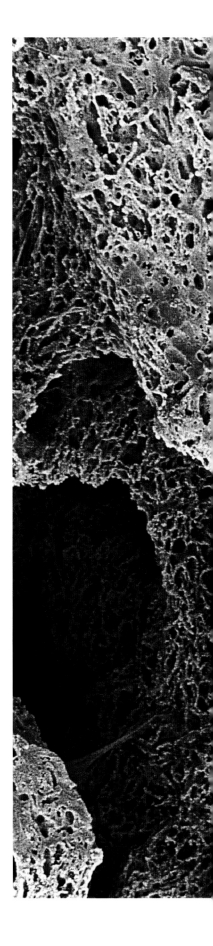

Entzündungs- und Knochenkrankheiten

Lebensgerüst

Les maladies inflammatoires et osseuses

La charpente de la vie

Inflammatory and bone diseases

The body's framework

Enfermedades inflamatorias y óseas

Pilares de la vida

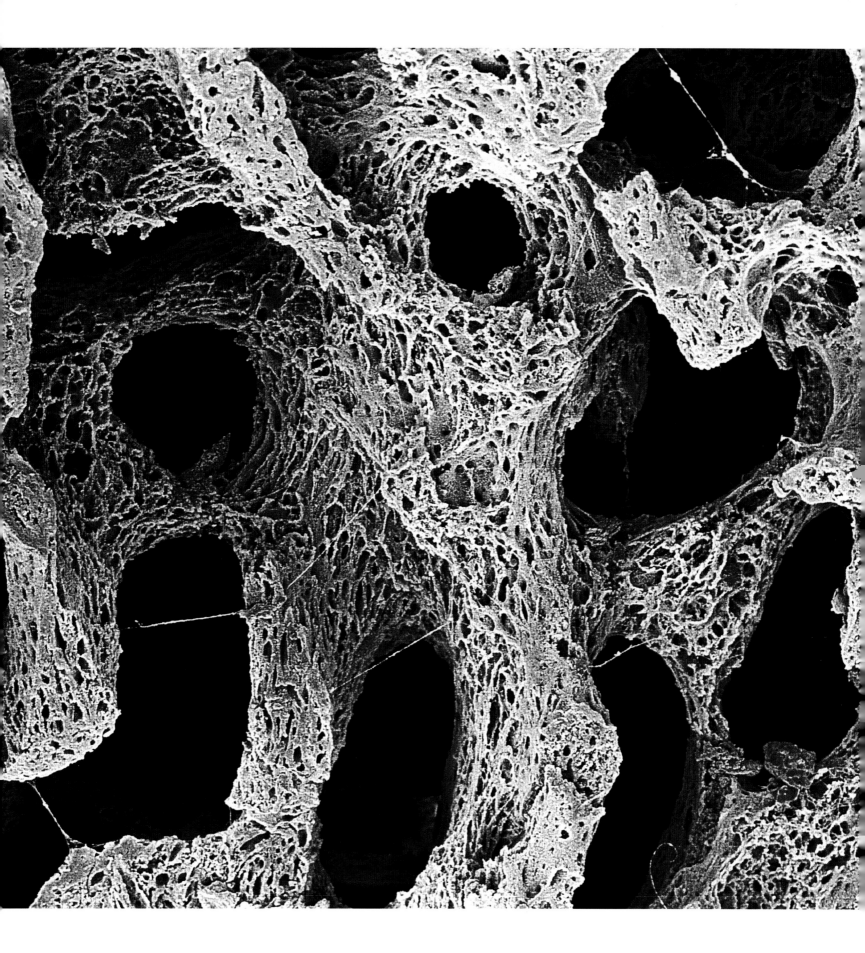

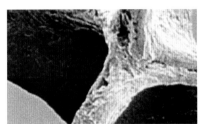

Knochen haben keine gute Presse, und unsere Sprache hat nicht viel für sie übrig. Knochen sind das, was zurückbleibt, wenn alles andere vergangen ist, und knochenschindend nennen wir das, was besondere Mühe macht.

Doch so belastend diese Sätze klingen, sie drücken auch aus, dass da etwas ist, auf das man sich am Ende wirklich verlassen kann – die Knochen nämlich. Dass auch sie anfällig für Krankheiten und Verletzungen sind, nimmt derjenige, der von Knochenbrüchen verschont bleibt, nur zögernd zur Kenntnis. Doch die Statistik spricht dagegen: Zum Beispiel bei mehr als 30 Prozent der Frauen, die über 50 Jahre alt sind, schwindet das feste Knochengewebe und wird durch hohle Markräume ersetzt. Mit der Osteoporose steigt auch das Risiko für traumatische Verletzungen an.

Wissenschaftler und Ärzte, die nach neuen Therapien suchen, hoffen darauf, genetische Faktoren zu finden, die die Knochenmasse und ihre Festigkeit bestimmen. Dieser Zugang allein wird aber nicht ausreichen, das ganze Geheimnis der Osteoporose zu entschlüsseln. Knochen machen zwar einen festen und unveränderlichen Eindruck, aber auch sie unterliegen einem dauernden Auf- und Abbau, der in ein doppeltes Gleichgewicht kommen muss. Es gilt nicht nur, das verloren gehende Material nachzuliefern. Beim kontinuierlichen Konstruieren der Knochen muss außerdem die Balance zwischen Ordnung und Unordnung gewahrt werden. Kontrolliertes Chaos ist notwendig, wenn wir stabil sein oder etwas Solides hervorbringen wollen.

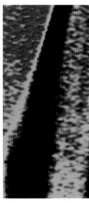

Les os n'ont pas bonne presse; des expressions telles que «ne pas faire de vieux os», «tomber sur un os» ou «n'avoir que la peau sur les os» en disent long sur les rapports que la langue entretient avec eux. Pour péjoratives que soient ces locutions, elles n'en laissent pas moins transparaître que les os sont, tout bien considéré, une chose à laquelle on peut se fier. Qu'ils puissent être sujets à des maladies ou des traumatismes est une réalité que les personnes suffisamment chanceuses pour ne jamais rien se briser ont parfois du mal à admettre. La statistique est pourtant formelle: plus de 30 pour cent des femmes de plus de 50 ans souffrent d'ostéoporose, c'est-à-dire d'une réduction de la masse osseuse entraînant un risque accru d'accidents traumatiques tels que fractures et tassements.

Scientifiques et médecins espèrent identifier les facteurs génétiques qui régulent la masse osseuse et dont dépend sa solidité. A elle seule, cette approche ne permettra toutefois pas de comprendre les mécanismes de l'ostéoporose. Donnant l'impression d'être infiniment robustes et invariables, les os n'en sont pas moins soumis à un processus constant de remaniement, où phases de résorption et phases de formation doivent doublement s'équilibrer. Il s'agit, en effet, de remplacer au fur et à mesure la matière osseuse détruite par la résorption, mais aussi de trouver, pour le processus en continu qu'est la formation de l'os, le juste milieu entre ordre et anarchie. Comme quoi un chaos contrôlé est tout indiqué pour construire quelque chose de stable et de solide.

PP. 94/95: Old osteoporotic bone. Computer-coloured scanning electron microscopy, Debbie Marshall, David Gregory/Wellcome Photo Library.

The body's framework

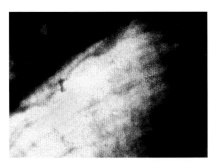

The word 'bone' has mixed connotations and does not feature in many expressions. Bones are what remains when everything else has been stripped away. Thus, one may 'work one's fingers to the bone', or be 'nothing but skin and bones'. As starkly physical as these figures of speech are, they express the simple truth that even if everything else is gone, we can still count on our bones. The fact that bones, too, are vulnerable and can suffer injury and disease scarcely enters the minds of people who have never suffered a fracture. In fact, statistics show that more than 30 percent of women over the age of 50 suffer from osteoporosis, that is to say, their solid bony tissue gradually disappears and is replaced by hollow marrow cavities. This increases the likelihood of traumatic injury to the bone.

In their efforts to develop new forms of treatment, doctors and scientists are hoping to identify genetic factors that play a role in determining bone density and strength. Nevertheless, the mystery of osteoporosis will not be unravelled by this approach alone. As solid and unchanging as bones may appear, they are in fact subject to a process of continuous synthesis and breakdown in which a double balance must be achieved: not only must the lost bone material be replaced, but the continuous remodelling process must be characterised by a balance between order and chaos. Controlled chaos is required in order to achieve stability and strength.

Pilares de la vida

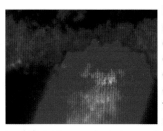

Los huesos no parecen gozar de buena prensa. El diccionario, por ejemplo, define «hueso» en sentido figurado como «algo que resulta difícil, que causa más trabajo que lo demás en cierta cosa, que es la parte más ingrata de un trabajo o que constituye una molestia». Pero por peyorativa que esta definición pueda parecer, deja traslucir también la idea del hueso como aquello que permanece cuando lo demás ya ha desaparecido, la idea del hueso como algo en lo que uno puede confiar. Que los huesos sean vulnerables y puedan enfermar o lesionarse es algo que sólo a duras penas parecen admitir los afortunados que jamás han sufrido una fractura. Los datos estadísticos, sin embargo, son bien elocuentes: más del 30 por ciento de las mujeres mayores de 50 años padecen osteoporosis, enfermedad caracterizada por una reducción de la masa ósea que se asocia a un aumento del riesgo de fracturas.

En sus esfuerzos por desarrollar nuevas modalidades terapéuticas, los científicos y los médicos confían en poder identificar los factores genéticos que determinan la densidad y la consistencia óseas. Pero ello solo no basta para desvelar por completo la patogenia de la osteoporosis. Por sólidos e inalterables que los huesos puedan parecer, lo cierto es que también ellos se hallan sometidos a un proceso continuo de síntesis y destrucción tendente a mantener un doble equilibrio: no sólo se trata, en efecto, de reemplazar el tejido óseo destruido, sino también de conseguir, en el continuo proceso de reestructuración ósea, el punto exacto de equilibrio entre orden y desorden. Un cierto grado de caos hace falta para construir solidez y estabilidad.

Entzündungs- und Knochenkrankheiten
Les maladies inflammatoires et osseuses
Inflammatory and bone diseases
Enfermedades inflamatorias y óseas

Ein dunkler Streifen mit blauen Farbtönen durchzieht eine grüne Fläche: Wir sehen die Form eines Knochens und erkennen deutlich das Mark im Inneren. Bilder wie dieses entstehen mit Hilfe der Magnetresonanztechnik und dienen den Wissenschaftlern dazu, die Festigkeit eines Knochens abzuschätzen. Die Muskeln, die an ihm angreifen und ihn bewegen, sind grün dargestellt. Der rote ellipsenförmige Hintergrund verleiht dem Bild seinen besonderen Reiz.

Le long cylindre sombre que l'on voit au centre de l'image est un fémur de rat. On distingue très bien, à l'intérieur, la moelle osseuse. Les images de ce genre, qui permettent aux chercheurs de se faire une idée de la solidité d'un os, sont obtenues par résonance magnétique. Les muscles qui sont insérés sur l'os et le font jouer apparaissent en vert. L'ensemble se détache sur une ellipse rouge du plus bel effet.

The dark stripe with shades of blue passing across a green surface indicates the shape of a bone. The marrow cavity within the bone is clearly visible. Using the technique of magnetic resonance imaging, researchers create images such as this in order to estimate the density of bones. The muscles that are attached to and move the bone appear green. The whole structure is shown on an elliptical red background that lends the image its charm.

Esta oscura banda azulada que vemos en el centro de la imagen corresponde a un hueso, un fémur de rata. En su interior se distingue claramente la médula ósea. La resonancia magnética nuclear permite obtener imágenes como ésta, gracias a las cuales los investigadores pueden valorar la solidez de un hueso. En verde pueden verse los músculos que se insertan en el fémur y lo movilizan. Todo ello enmarcado por una hermosa elipse roja.

Rat femur. Magnetic resonance microscopy, Markus von Kienlin, Volker Elste, Stephanie Schoeppenthau, Thomas Bielser, Basil Kuennecke, Roche Basel.

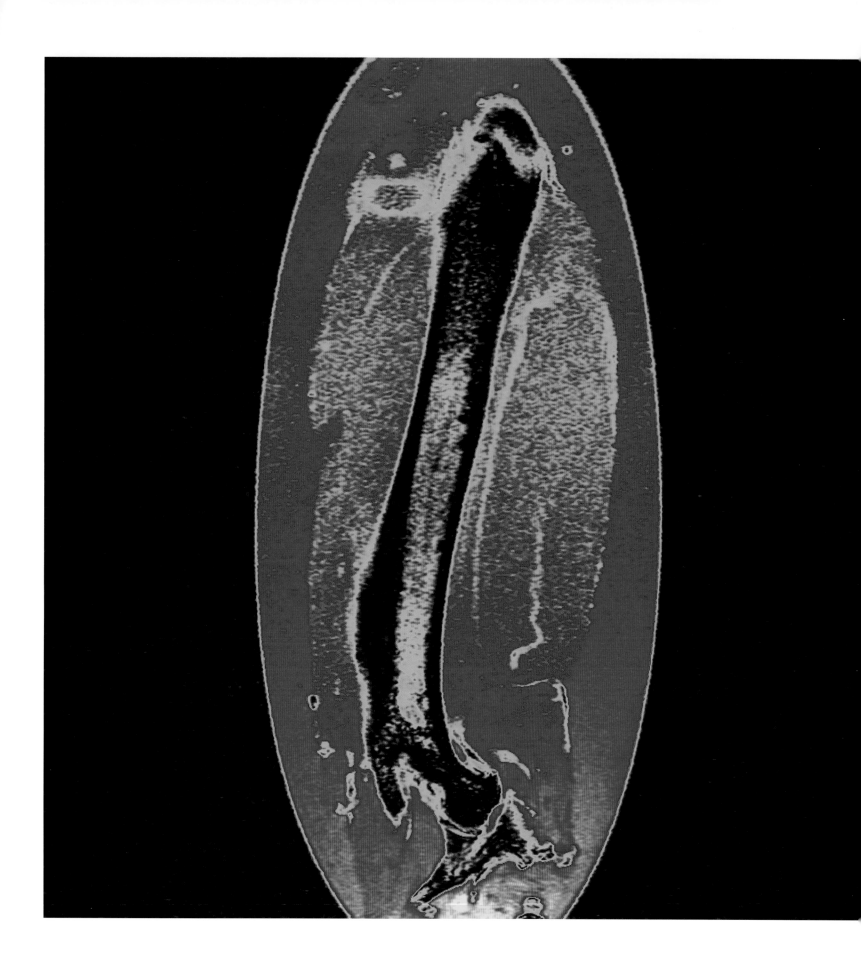

Entzündungs- und Knochenkrankheiten
Les maladies inflammatoires et osseuses
Inflammatory and bone diseases
Enfermedades inflamatorias y óseas

Was uns als eine ungeheuer bewegliche und offenbar auch bewegte Struktur vor Augen tritt, stellt in Wirklichkeit ein Musterbeispiel für Starre und Festigkeit dar: der Oberschenkelknochen (Femur), hier im Querschnitt, erinnert an eine spiegelnde Wasseroberfläche und beweist, dass es in der Natur nichts Langweiliges gibt. Was zum Leben gehört, zeigt sich uns immer lebendig.

Ce qui apparaît comme une structure extraordinairement mouvante et mouvementée et évoque un rayon de soleil se reflétant dans l'eau est, en réalité, un modèle de rigidité et de solidité. Il s'agit d'un fémur ou, pour être précis, d'une coupe de ce gros os. Cette image apporte une fois de plus la preuve que rien de ce qui existe dans la nature n'est ennuyeux et que ce qui fait partie de la vie se manifeste toujours sous des formes vivantes.

This tremendously fluid and apparently turbulent structure immediately suggests gleaming ripples on water. In fact, it represents the epitome of rigidity and firmness – the thigh bone, or femur. This cross-section reminds us that there is no monotony in nature. All living things reveal their life to us at every moment.

Esto que parece una estructura tremendamente móvil y agitada, evocadora de los reflejos luminosos que se forman en el agua, corresponde en realidad al ejemplo arquetípico de rigidez y solidez: un hueso. Este corte transversal de un fémur es un nuevo ejemplo de que nada hay en la naturaleza que sea monótono. Todo cuanto forma parte de la vida se nos muestra siempre vivo.

Cross-section of the thigh bone (femur). Polarised microscopy, Wellcome Photo Library.

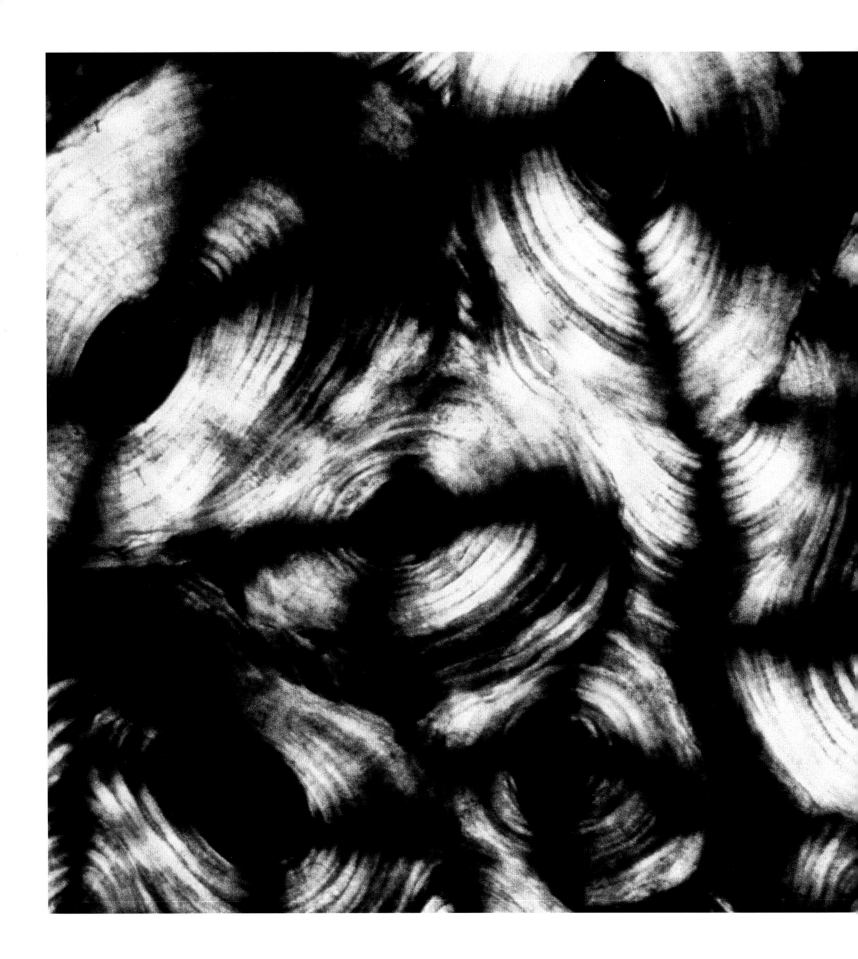

Entzündungs- und Knochenkrankheiten
Les maladies inflammatoires et osseuses
Inflammatory and bone diseases
Enfermedades inflamatorias y óseas

In aller Schlichtheit sehen wir das Modell eines Wirkstoffs mit Namen Ibandronat, der als Medikament gegen Osteoporose zum Einsatz kommt. Das Modell lässt ein inneres Gerüst von verbundenen Molekülen erkennen, das die äußere Form vorgibt. Um dieses Gerüst legen sich wolkenartig die kleineren Bausteine, die zur Gesamtstruktur gehören. Wir sehen die Oberfläche so, wie sie sich einem anderen Molekül präsentiert, das mit dem Ibandronat in Kontakt tritt.

Modèle d'une substance active appelée ibandronate, que l'on donne aux personnes atteintes d'ostéoporose. On reconnaît distinctement la charpente intérieure, formée de molécules liées les unes aux autres, qui donne sa forme à l'ensemble. Autour de cette charpente s'articulent, comme une formation nuageuse, les éléments plus petits de la structure. On voit ici la surface telle qu'elle se présente aux autres molécules cherchant à entrer en contact avec l'ibandronate.

Here is a simple model of a compound called ibandronate, which is used to treat osteoporosis. The model displays the internal framework of linked molecules that determine the compound's basic shape. Floating cloud-like around this framework are the smaller components that flesh out the overall structure. The view seen here shows the surface as presented to other molecules about to interact with ibandronate.

En esta imagen destaca la sencillez del modelo estructural de un fármaco llamado ibandronato, para el tratamiento de la osteoporosis. Se reconoce con nitidez la estructura lineal interna de moléculas ligadas entre sí, que determinan la forma básica del conjunto. En torno a esta armazón central se disponen, flotando como nubes, los elementos más pequeños de la estructura, de tal modo que puede verse la superficie tal y como ésta se presenta a las moléculas que han de entrar en contacto con el ibandronato.

Ibandronate. Frank Grams, Roche Basel.

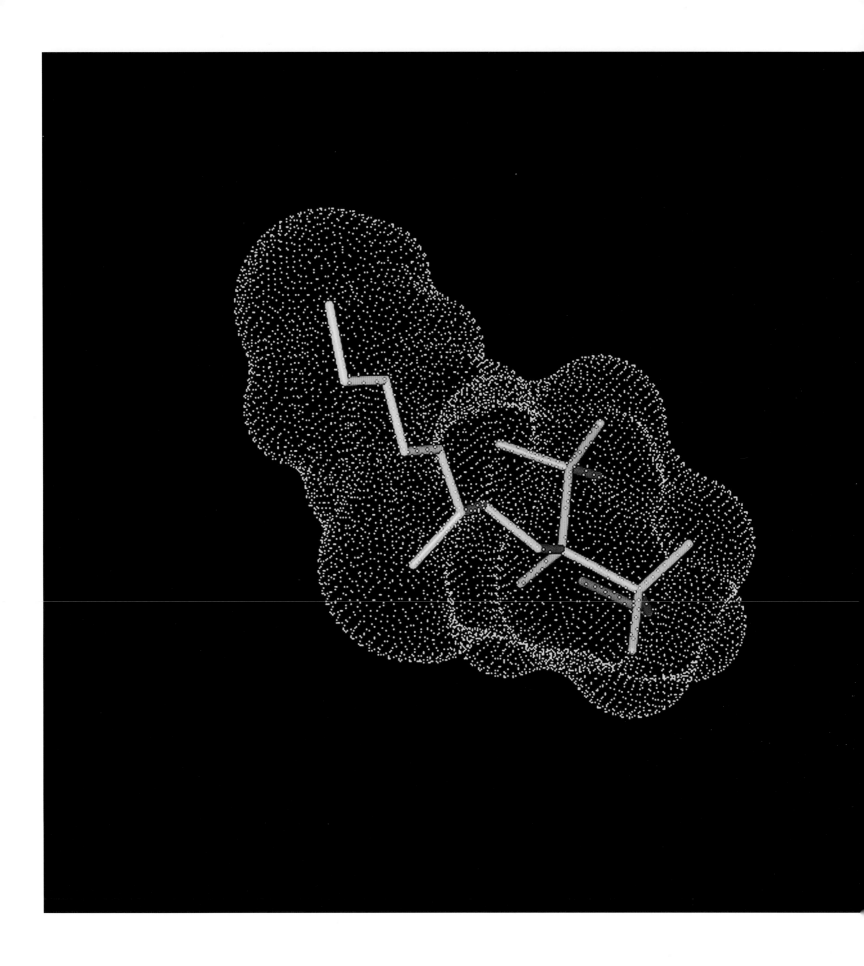

Entzündungs- und Knochenkrankheiten
Les maladies inflammatoires et osseuses
Inflammatory and bone diseases
Enfermedades inflamatorias y óseas

Der Blick mit dem Elektronenmikroskop in das Innere eines durch Osteoporose beeinträchtigten Knochens zeigt mehr Lücken als feste Verbindungen. Dem wissenschaftlich bewaffneten Auge erschließt sich ein höchst fragiles Gerüst, das selbst der kleinsten Belastung nicht mehr standhalten kann. Den stärksten Schwund der Knochensubstanz zeigen die blinden Enden, die ins Leere laufen und keinen Kontakt mehr zustande bringen.

L'œil que le microscope électronique fait pénétrer à l'intérieur d'un os endommagé par l'ostéoporose découvre plus de trous que de traverses assurant sa solidité. Un regard exercé reconnaît aussitôt une charpente hautement fragilisée, pour laquelle la moindre sollicitation serait de trop. Les prolongements osseux qui se perdent dans le vide, sans ne plus établir aucun contact, montrent à quel point la raréfaction de la substance osseuse peut être importante.

A view through an electron microscope into the interior of an osteoporotic bone reveals more gaps than solid structure. The trained, scientific eye encounters extremely fragile scaffolding incapable of supporting even the slightest additional load. The fact that some of the structural elements peter out into dead ends shows the extent of the loss of bone substance.

Si contemplamos a través del microscopio electrónico el interior de un hueso afectado de osteoporosis, descubriremos más huecos que estructuras sólidas. El ojo experto del científico reconoce, además, la fragilidad de las estructuras óseas, incapaces de resistir la mínima carga. Las prolongaciones óseas que mueren en el vacío sin llegar a establecer contacto ponen de manifiesto la magnitud de la pérdida de sustancia ósea.

Vertical section through an osteoporotic lumbar vertebral body. Scanning electron microscopy, Allan Boyde/Wellcome Photo Library.

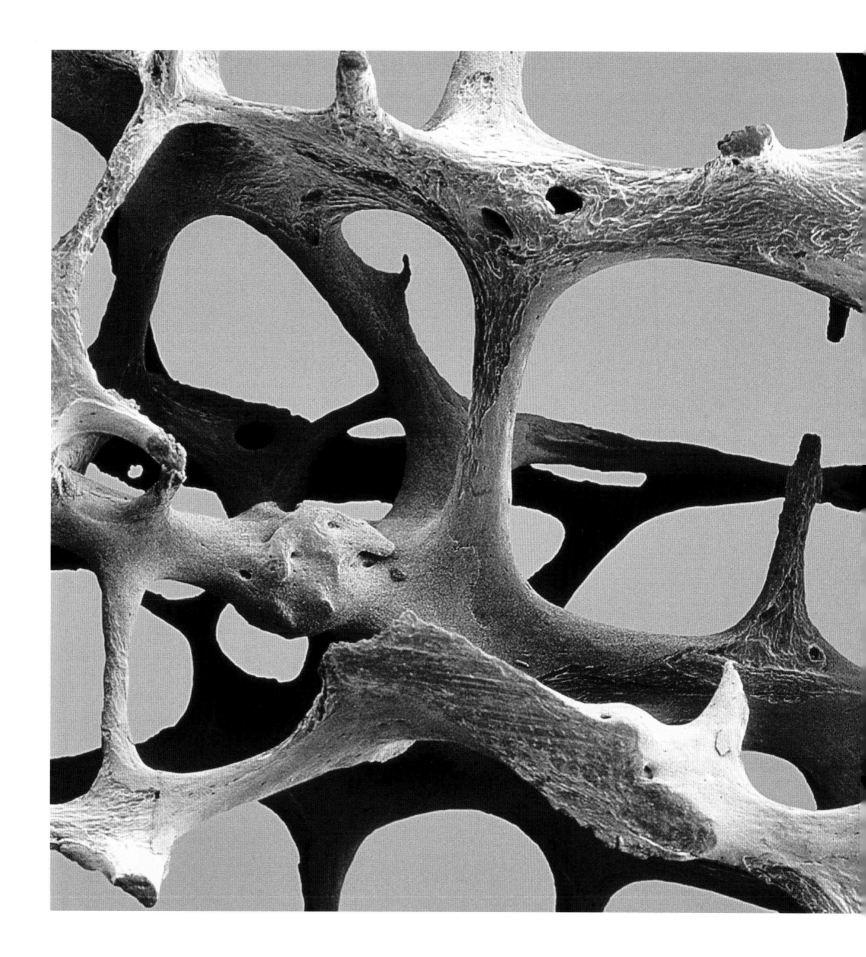

Entzündungs- und Knochenkrankheiten
Les maladies inflammatoires et osseuses
Inflammatory and bone diseases
Enfermedades inflamatorias y óseas

Dieses Farbenspiel markiert die breite funktionelle Verzweigung eines Hüftknochens. Der Weg der Farben führt vom warmen Rot über das Gelbe und Grüne zum kühlen Blau, das sich deutlich in einen hellen und einen dunklen Teil spaltet. Der weiße Fleck im Mittelpunkt steht als Sammelpunkt der Farben auch im Zentrum des Knochens.

Ce que l'on voit ici est une portion de la crête iliaque, autrement dit de l'un des deux os formant, avec le sacrum, le bassin. Le regard est tout de suite accroché par le ton chaud du rouge, et c'est seulement après que, passant par le jaune et le vert, il s'intéresse au bleu, beaucoup plus froid et se scindant nettement en une partie claire et une partie foncée. La tache blanche, au milieu de l'image, autour de laquelle se rassemblent les couleurs, est aussi le centre de l'os.

The bright colours seen here indicate the broad functional divisions of a piece of hip bone. The viewer's eyes follow the path of colours from the warm red through the yellow and green to the cool blue end of the spectrum, which is clearly divided into light and dark areas. The white area in the middle is both the focal point of the colours and the centre of the bone.

Este juego de colores revela la compleja división funcional de una muestra ósea tomada de la cadera. La cálida tonalidad del rojo capta de inmediato la mirada del observador, que sólo después se dirige, a través del amarillo y el verde, hacia la zona azul más fría, claramente dividida en una parte oscura y otra clara. La blanca mancha central constituye no sólo el centro de los colores, sino también el centro del hueso.

A piece of bone from the iliac crest of a human pelvis. Scanning electron microscopy, Allan Boyde/Wellcome Photo Library.

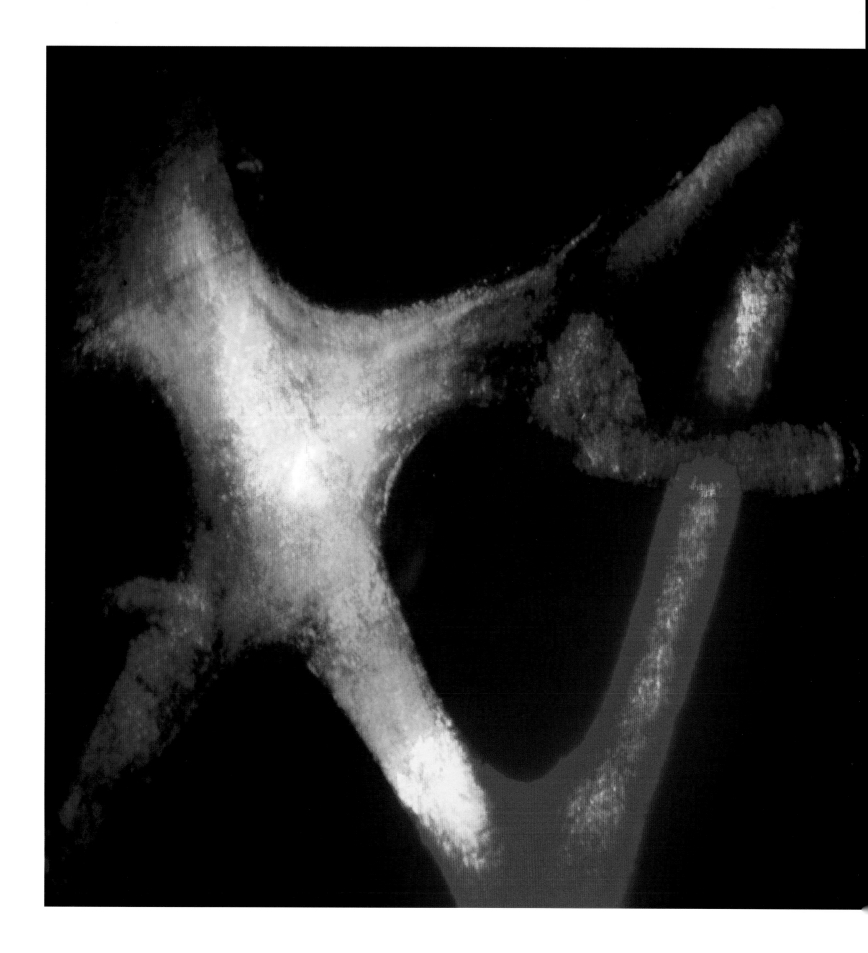

Entzündungs- und Knochenkrankheiten
Les maladies inflammatoires et osseuses
Inflammatory and bone diseases
Enfermedades inflamatorias y óseas

Wenn man einen Kristall mit seinen periodischen Strukturen mit Hilfe von Elektronen «durchleuchtet» und die abgelenkten Strahlen auf einem Schirm sichtbar macht, erhält man ein Muster von Punkten – das so genannte Beugungsmuster. Damit kann berechnet werden, wie die Bestandteile des analysierten Kristalls angeordnet sind. Was wie der Blick in den Himmel über uns und damit in die Außenwelt erscheint, macht in Wirklichkeit die Innenwelt zugänglich.

Voilà ce qu'on obtient lorsqu'on «radiographie» un cristal et ses structures périodiques à l'aide d'électrons et que l'on fait apparaître les rayons lumineux sur un écran. On appelle modèle de diffraction ce motif en forme de points. Il permet de calculer la façon dont sont disposés les éléments du cristal que l'on étudie. Alors qu'on a l'impression de voir la voûte céleste et de s'élever dans l'espace, cette image donne en réalité accès à un monde on ne peut plus intérieur.

By passing electrons through the repetitive structure of a crystal and rendering the deflected rays visible on a screen, we obtain a pattern of spots – a diffraction pattern – such as that seen here. This can be used to calculate the arrangement of the components of the crystal. What looks like a view of the sky, and thus of the outer world, is in fact a view of an inner world.

Esta imagen punteada corresponde a lo que los científicos llaman un «difractograma electrónico», que se obtiene atravesando con electrones la repetitiva estructura de un cristal y registrando los rayos desviados en una pantalla. Los investigadores se sirven de los difractogramas para determinar la disposición de los componentes del cristal analizado. Lo que parece una vista de la bóveda celeste o el espacio sideral, nos abre en realidad las puertas a un mundo interior.

Crystal structure. Electron diffractogram, Françoise Gerber, Bernd Bohrmann, Roche Basel.

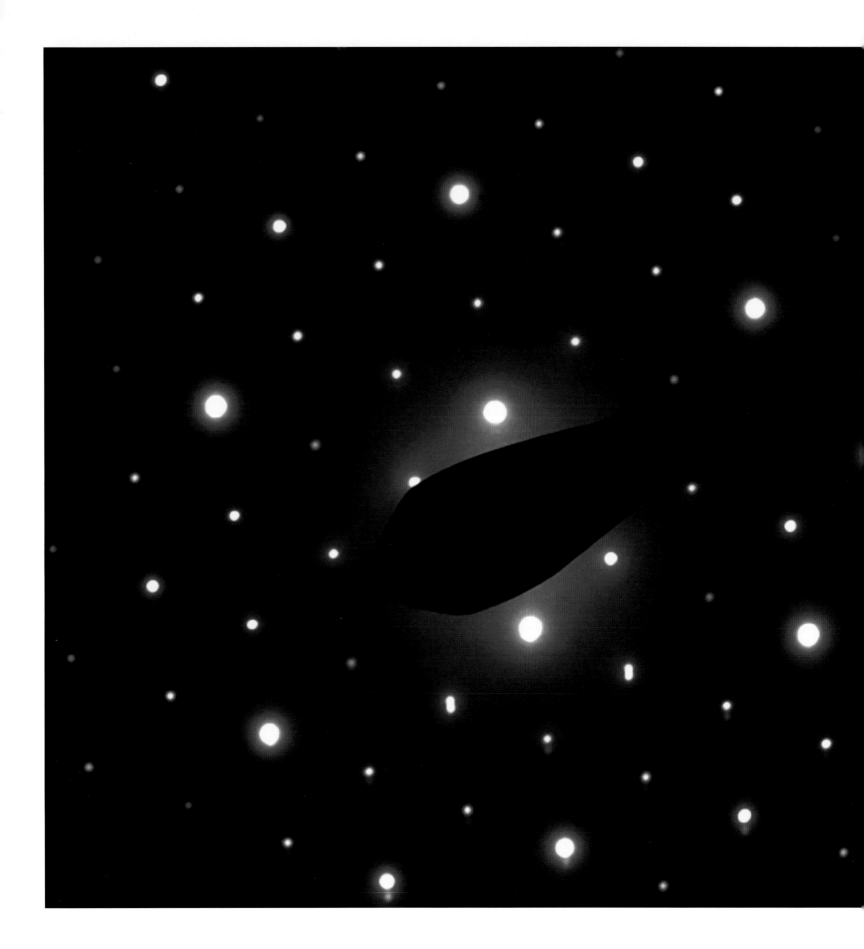

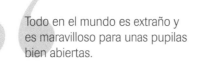
Virologie

Grenzleben

La virologie

Aux frontières de la vie

Virology

Life at the threshold

Virología

En las fronteras de la vida

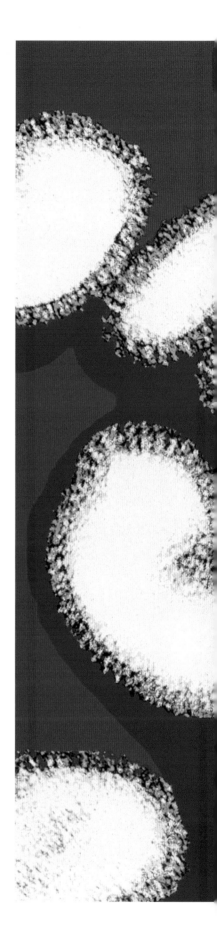

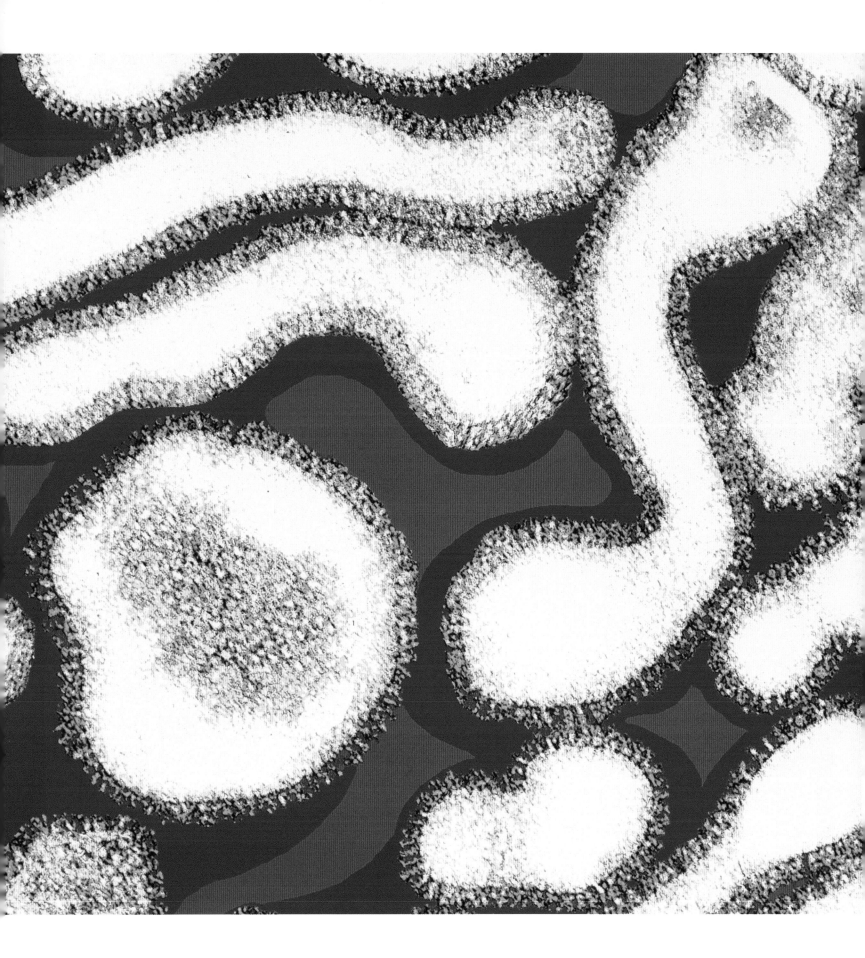

Grenzleben

Aux frontières de la vie

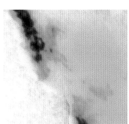 Wer Viren untersucht, lässt sich auf Strukturen ein, die an der Grenze zum Leben stehen. «Lebendige Moleküle» – so nannte Wendell Stanley in den dreißiger Jahren des letzten Jahrhunderts die Gebilde, die er bei seinen frühen Untersuchungen von Viren, die Tabakpflanzen befallen, entdeckte. Es war die Regelmäßigkeit der Tabakmosaikviren, die den Wissenschaftlern zunächst auffiel. Inzwischen sind zahlreiche Strukturen vieler anderer Viren bekannt geworden, und immer wieder zeigen sich neue und überraschende Formvarianten, die uns eine Ahnung davon vermitteln, welcher Spielraum der Evolution zur Verfügung steht.

Die Technik erlaubt uns heute, viele Bilder von Viren zu erzeugen, und als Folge davon können wir uns auch ein Bild davon machen, was Viren überhaupt sind. Das heißt, wir können mit Hilfe der Bilder die Viren untersuchen. Die wissenschaftlichen und immer auch schönen Bilder übernehmen in der Forschung die Rolle, die das Sehen im Alltag hat. Mit dem Sehen und der durch die Augen vermittelten Wahrnehmung beginnt das Denken. Dabei sollte man sich klarmachen, dass das Sehen weniger ein Fotografieren und mehr ein Malen ist. Es geht also nicht um «pictures», sondern um «images» und die dazugehörenden Imaginationen, weniger um Abbildungen als um Vorstellungen – wie es der Titel des vorliegenden Buchs ausdrückt.

Dass Sehen erst der Anfang von Wahrnehmung ist, liegt daran, dass im Gehirn das, was die Augen liefern, in Punkte, Linien, Winkel und mehr zerlegt wird, wie die moderne Neurophysiologie nachgewiesen hat. Im Kopf muss daraus dann geformt werden, was wir sehen. Das Gehirn geht also wie ein Maler vor, der Punkte, Linien, Winkel und mehr auf die Leinwand bringt. Wenn wir das Bild betrachten, setzen wir außen bewusst fort, was innen unbewusst längst begonnen hat. Wenn wir aus den Bildern der Forschung lernen, tun wir also, was uns die Natur mit den Bildern im Gehirn beigebracht hat.

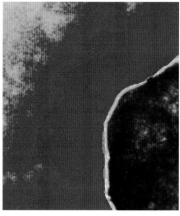 Etudier des virus, c'est étudier des structures se situant aux frontières du vivant. Des «molécules vivantes», disait Wendell Stanley dans les années 1930, parlant des virus qui attaquent le tabac. Ce qui frappait alors les scientifiques était la régularité que présentait la structure du virus de la mosaïque du tabac. Au fur et à mesure que se sont enrichies nos connaissances de ces agents pathogènes est apparue une diversité de formes laissant deviner la marge de manœuvre sur laquelle peut compter l'évolution pour accomplir son destin.

Grâce aux progrès de la technique, on a aujourd'hui la possibilité d'étudier les virus à travers les images qu'on sait en faire. Toujours très belles, ces images scientifiques sont aux chercheurs ce que les yeux sont au commun des mortels. C'est-à-dire que les perceptions induites par la vue donnent naissance à la réflexion. A noter qu'il ne s'agit pas, en l'occurrence, d'une vision photographique mais picturale, pas d'instantanés, mais d'images au sens où elles sont produites par l'imagination, comme le sous-entend le titre de ce livre.

La raison en est que, comme on le sait grâce à la neurophysiologie moderne, le cerveau décompose les éléments fournis par l'œil en points, lignes, angles et autres figures, à partir desquels est ensuite formé ce que l'on voit. Le cerveau procède comme le peintre qui met sur la toile des points, des lignes et des angles. Lorsqu'on contemple le résultat, se poursuit consciement, en dehors de soi, ce qui, inconsciemment, avait commencé depuis longtemps au-dedans. Quand le chercheur se sert d'images pour élargir ses connaissances, il fait donc ce que la nature lui appris à faire avec les images.

PP. 110/111: Coloured influenza viruses. Transmission electron microscopy, Keystone/Linda Stannard/UCT.

Life at the threshold

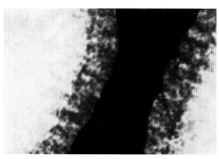

In studying viruses, we are looking at structures that stand at the very threshold of life. 'Living molecules' was the phrase used by Wendell Stanley in the 1930s to describe the structures that he encountered in his early studies on viruses that affect tobacco plants. The first thing that struck scientists about the tobacco mosaic virus was its regularity. Since then, the molecular structures of many other viruses have been elucidated, revealing ever more surprising variations in form. This gives us an inkling as to the huge range of variation available for evolution.

Modern techniques allow us to make all sorts of images of viruses, and we can use these images to construct our own image of what viruses are, in other words, to investigate viruses. Scientific – and at the same time beautiful – images play the same role in research as our eyes do in everyday life. Eyesight and the perception that arises from it form the basis of thought. In this respect we must always be aware that eyesight is more akin to painting than to photography. In other words, what it generates is not pictures, but rather images and imagination, as expressed in the title of this book.

Research in neurophysiology has shown that this is because the brain breaks down the information supplied to it by the eyes into points, lines and other forms. From this information it has to construct images of what we see. The brain thus acts in the manner of a painter who applies points, lines and forms to a canvas. Observation of the resulting image is a conscious continuation of a process that began far earlier at an unconscious level. In learning from scientific images, we are therefore doing precisely what nature has taught us to do with the images in our minds.

En las fronteras de la vida

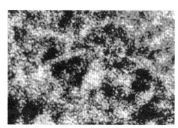

Estudiar los virus es estudiar estructuras situadas en las fronteras de la vida. De «moléculas vivas» hablaba Wendell Stanley en el decenio 1930–39 para referirse a los virus que afectaban a la planta del tabaco. Lo que más llamaba la atención de los científicos era la regularidad estructural que presentaba el virus del mosaico del tabaco. Desde entonces hemos ido descubriendo la estructura de muchos otros virus, y la diversidad de formas sorprendentes nos permite hacernos una idea del amplio margen de maniobra de que ha dispuesto la evolución.

Los avances de la técnica nos ofrecen la posibilidad de obtener numerosas imágenes de los virus, gracias a las cuales podemos formarnos también, y valga el juego de palabras, una imagen de los virus. Científicas y a un tiempo hermosas, las imágenes son para los investigadores lo mismo que la vista para el resto de las personas. Las percepciones que recibimos a través de los ojos son el origen del pensamiento. Es de destacar, en cualquier caso, que no se trata tanto de una percepción fotográfica como de una percepción pictórica; es decir, no de «instantáneas», sino más bien de «imágenes» en las que interviene la imaginación, como deja traslucir el título del presente libro.

La neurofisiología moderna ha demostrado que el cerebro descompone la información suministrada por el ojo en puntos, líneas, ángulos y otras figuras diversas, a partir de las cuales forma en nuestra cabeza lo que vemos. El cerebro se comporta, pues, como un pintor que traza sobre el lienzo puntos, líneas, ángulos y demás. Cuando contemplamos el resultado, efectuamos fuera de forma consciente lo que de forma inconsciente llevábamos mucho tiempo efectuando dentro. Cuando un científico aprovecha las imágenes para aprender algo nuevo, no hace más que lo que la naturaleza le ha enseñado a hacer con cualquier imagen en el cerebro.

Auf den ersten Blick mag es zwar so aussehen, also ob die Menschen der Grippe hilflos ausgeliefert wären – keine Infektionskrankheit sucht uns historisch gesehen länger heim –, aber auf den zweiten Blick bekommen wir immer besser die Bestandteile des Virus in den wissenschaftlichen Griff. Und mit dieser zunehmend tiefer dringenden Kenntnis können wir uns zur Wehr setzen. Das Bild zeigt den Ausschnitt des Proteins Neuraminidase, das wesentlich für das Funktionieren des Virus ist. Das mit Hilfe von Röntgenanalysen ermittelte Modell besteht aus Bändern und Pfeilen, die in allen Spektralfarben leuchten. In der Mitte wurde eine Ansammlung von meist violetten Kugeln platziert. Um sie dreht sich die Fantasie der Forscher, ihre Imagination. Die bunten Kugeln stellen das Modell des Medikaments dar, mit dem sie besagtes Molekül gezielt besetzen wollen, um auf diese Weise das ganze Virus lahmzulegen.

L'homme est apparemment toujours aussi démuni devant la grippe, ancêtre historique des maladies infectieuses. Mais lorsqu'on y regarde de plus près, on constate que les scientifiques connaissent de mieux en mieux les éléments du virus qui la cause. Et au fur et à mesure que ces connaissances s'approfondissent se développent des parades. Cette image offre une vue partielle d'une protéine, la neuraminidase, essentielle au bon fonctionnement du virus. Déterminé à l'aide d'analyses aux rayons X, le modèle de cette substance que l'on voit ici se présente sous forme de rubans et de flèches resplendissant de toutes les couleurs du spectre. Au centre, un amas de sphères violettes, autour desquelles gravite l'imagination des chercheurs et qui représentent le médicament censé investir la molécule et paralyser le virus.

At first sight it may seem that human beings are completely defenceless against influenza, since no infectious disease has afflicted us over a longer period of our history. In fact, scientists are acquiring an ever deeper knowledge of the components of the influenza virus, and, armed with this knowledge, we can fight back. This image shows part of a protein (neuraminidase) that plays an important role in the life of the influenza virus. This model, which was produced by x-ray analysis, is made up of interconnecting bands and arrows in all the colours of the rainbow. In the centre is a collection of mostly purple spheres. Around these revolves the imagination of the scientists who produced the image. The brightly coloured spheres represent a drug – a neuraminidase inhibitor – that scientists hope will attach to a specific site on the neuraminidase molecule and thereby paralyse the entire virus.

A primera vista, puede parecer que el ser humano se halla indefenso frente a la gripe, la más antigua de las enfermedades infecciosas. Pero cuando uno profundiza un poco advierte que, en realidad, los científicos conocen cada vez mejor la estructura de su virus causal. Y conforme avanzan nuestros conocimientos, avanzan también nuestras posibilidades defensivas. En la imagen puede apreciarse parte de una proteína, la neraminidasa, esencial para el funcionamiento del virus. Este modelo, obtenido mediante análisis radiocristalográfico, consta de cintas y flechas multicolores que reproducen todo el cromatismo del arco iris. En el centro puede verse un amasijo de esferas de color violeta, en torno al cual giran la fantasía y la imaginación de los investigadores. Estas esferas constituyen el modelo de un medicamento destinado a inhibir la molécula de neraminidasa y paralizar el virus por completo.

Molscript ribbon drawing of the monomer subunit of N9 influenza neuraminidase. X-ray crystallography, Bradford Graves, Roche Welwyn.

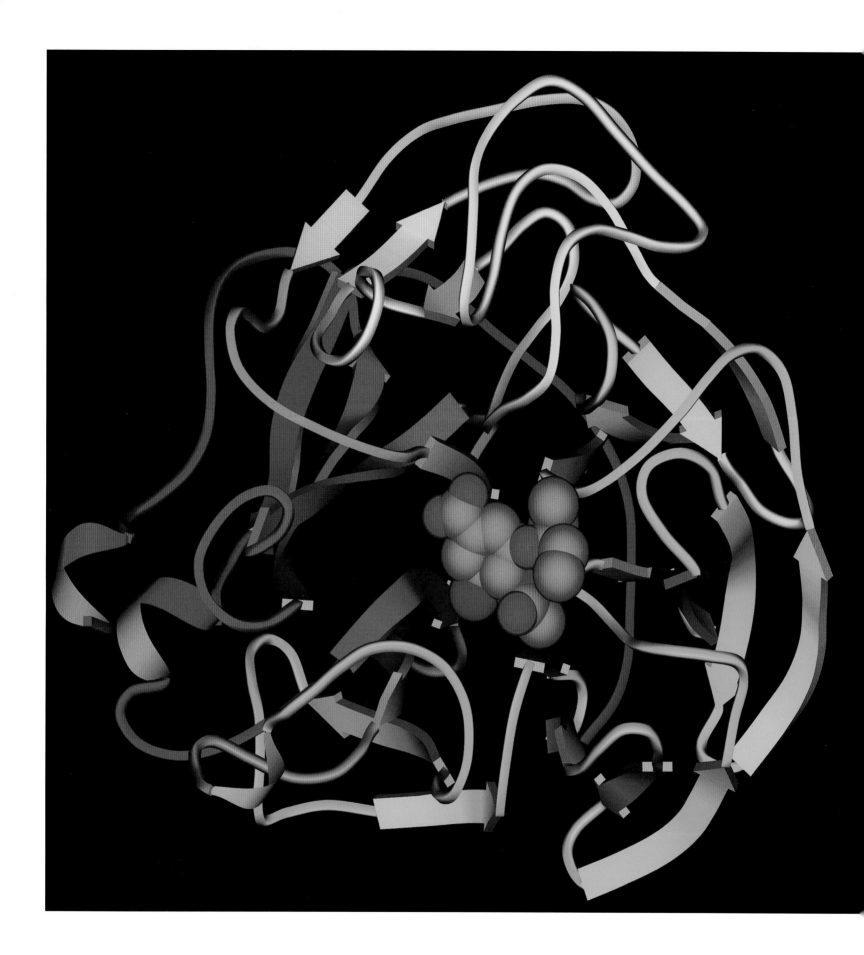

Was hier ins Auge sticht und gelblich rund vor einem schwarzvioletten Hintergrund zu sehen ist, fürchten wir vor allem, wenn es kalt wird und der Winter naht. Grippeviren sind es, Influenzaviren, wie sie in der Fachsprache heißen. So banal es sich anhört, wenn wir sagen, jemand kuriert seine Grippe aus, so alarmiert muss die Wissenschaft sein, wenn die Influenza naht. Die Grippe ist die älteste bekannte Epidemie. Sie breitet sich seit dem Mittelalter mit boshafter Regelmäßigkeit aus, und immer noch gibt es kein Mittel, das sie daran hindert. Nach wie vor behält sie ihr genetisches Geheimnis, und so ist sie mehr als die launige «Grille», die das französische Wort ausdrückt, von dem unser deutscher Ausdruck «Grippe» stammt.

Ces trois formes arrondies, d'un jaune pâle tranchant sur un fond bleu virant au noir, sont des virus de la grippe, ou de l'influenza, ceux-là même qui nous guettent sitôt que le temps se met au froid et que s'annonce l'hiver. Si banale que soit la grippe, son approche est toujours un moment qui met en émoi le monde des sciences médicales. Les épidémies de grippe sont les plus anciennes que l'on connaisse. Depuis le moyen âge, elles sévissent toujours avec la même virulence et la même régularité, et personne n'a encore trouvé le moyen de les en empêcher. Le mystère génétique de la maladie reste entier et le nom de grippe, qu'on lui donne parce qu'elle saisit brusquement ses victimes, la dépeint toujours aussi bien.

The rounded yellow structures seen here against a dark purple background are influenza viruses, something we especially fear as winter approaches. However self-evident it may seem to us that we will always 'get over the flu', the approach of this pernicious infection – the oldest known epidemic disease – is always a cause for alarm among scientists. Outbreaks of influenza have occurred with monotonous regularity ever since the Middle Ages, and to this day nobody has found a way of preventing them. By guarding its genetic secrets, the influenza virus has retained a destructive capacity far exceeding that suggested by the Italian word for 'influence', from which it derives its name.

Estas formas redondeadas y amarillentas que destacan vivamente sobre el fondo violeta y negro, resultan temibles cuando la temperatura refresca y se aproxima el invierno. Se trata, en efecto, de los virus de la gripe. Por banal que parezca la gripe, su proximidad causa siempre alarma en los ambientes científico-médicos. Las epidemias de gripe son las más antiguas de que se tiene noticia. Desde la Edad Media vienen repitiéndose con parecida regularidad y virulencia, sin que nadie hasta ahora haya sido capaz de impedirlo, ni de desvelar tampoco su secreto genético.

Influenza virus. Transmission electron microscopy, Charles Craig, Roche Welwyn.

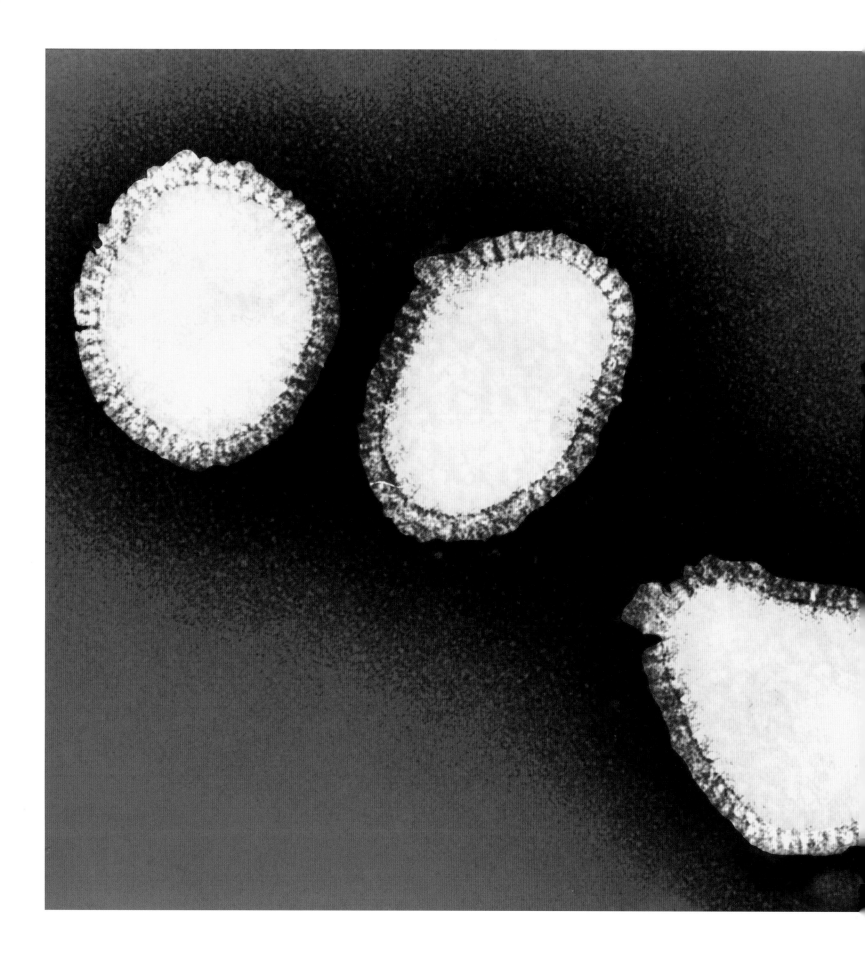

Viele kleine rote Kreise, die nur angedeutet erscheinen und zusammen einen größeren Kreis bilden, in dem ein einsamer Punkt auf einer gelben Fläche sichtbar wird. Was wie eine lockere Skizze wirkt, zeigt in der mikroskopischen Wirklichkeit eine Gruppe von Aids-Viren. Sie haben sich auf der Oberfläche der Zelle niedergelassen, die sie zu ihrer Vermehrung brauchen. Man nennt sie die Helfer-Zelle, und ihre hoffnungslose Lage offenbart sich uns in einer Aufnahme, die mit dem Elektronenmikroskop erstellt und mit so genannten Pseudofarben aufbereitet worden ist.

Une multitude de petits ronds de couleur rouge, à peine esquissés, formant en se combinant un cercle où se détache, sur fond jaune, un point isolé. Ce qui apparaît au microscope comme une simple ébauche est en réalité un groupe de virus du sida colonisant la surface de la cellule dont ils ont besoin pour se multiplier. Cette cellule est une cellule T auxiliaire (ou helper en anglais), et l'image au microscope électronique préparée en pseudocoloration que l'on voit ici en dit long sur le sort qui l'attend.

A group of scarcely discernible small red circles together make up a larger circle in which a solitary point is seen on a yellow surface. What looks like a casually executed sketch is in fact the appearance under the microscope of a group of human immunodeficiency viruses that have attached themselves to the surface of a cell before penetrating it so that they can replicate. The hopeless situation of the attacked T-helper cell is apparent in this image, which was produced with the aid of an electron microscope and pseudocolours.

Sobre el fondo amarillo, varios anillos punteados de color rojo, apenas esbozados, forman en conjunto un gran círculo en torno a una estructura circular central. Esto que en el microscopio parece poco más que un esbozo, es en realidad un grupo de virus del sida que invaden la superficie de la célula que necesitan para reproducirse. Se trata más concretamente de un linfocito T auxiliar, que parece condenado a una muerte segura, a juzgar por esta imagen obtenida mediante microscopia electrónica con un método de seudocoloración.

Human immunodeficiency viruses on the surface of a T-helper lymphocyte. Transmission electron microscopy, Bernd Bohrmann, Roche Basel.

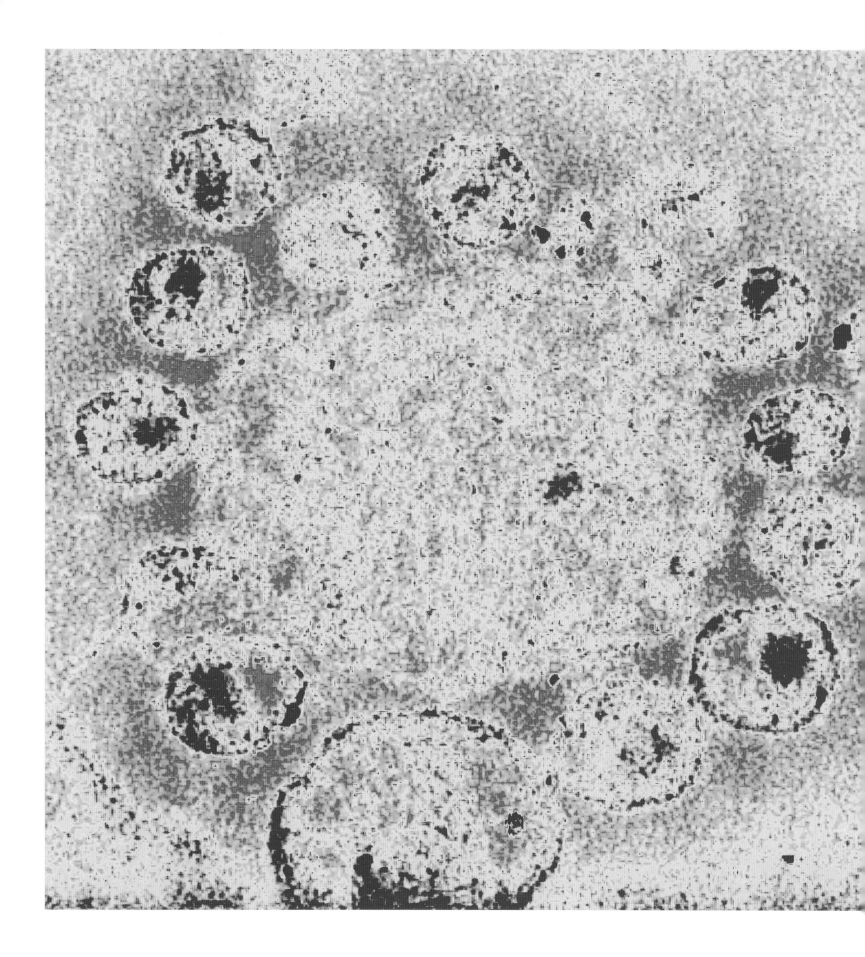

Eine bunte Lichtervielfalt, die den Teilbereich, eine Domäne, eines Proteins zeigt, das in allen menschlichen Zellen zu finden ist. Es handelt sich um eine so genannte Kinase, die im Zellinneren Signale übermittelt und dadurch andere Proteine aktiviert. Um Virologie geht es hier nur indirekt, denn die Kenntnis der gezeigten Struktur kann umfassend genutzt werden. Proteine wie die Kinase bestehen aus Aminosäuren, die zu Ketten zusammengefügt werden. Die Natur kann dabei zwischen zwanzig Aminosäuren wählen. In der Abbildung haben alle, die in dieser Domäne vorkommen, ihre eigene Farbe bekommen. Sie sind weiss, rot, grün, hell- und dunkelblau und noch anders gezeichnet. Der unruhige Eindruck, den das Bild macht, spricht für seine Qualität: Proteine müssen nämlich flexibel sein, um zu funktionieren.

Apparaissant dans un chatoiement multicolore de lumière, un domaine, c'est-à-dire un niveau de structure d'une protéine présente dans toutes les cellules de l'organisme humain. Il s'agit d'une kinase, dont les signaux sont capables d'activer d'autres protéines. Ce qui intéresse ici le virologue est avant tout la structure et les points d'impact qu'elle peut offrir à des médicaments. La kinase est constituée d'acides aminés formant des chaînes. La nature a le choix entre vingt acides aminés. Ceux que l'on voit dans le segment représenté par cette image ont chacun une couleur différente: blanc, rouge, vert, bleu clair et bleu foncé. L'impression d'agitation que l'on a en les regardant est en fait une qualité: les protéines ont besoin d'être libres aux entournures pour bien fonctionner.

This profusion of colours represents part (a domain) of a kinase, a class of proteins present in all human cells. Kinases transmit signals within cells and thereby activate other proteins. This image is related to virology only indirectly, in that knowledge of this structure has broad applications. Proteins such as kinases consist of chains of amino acids. In nature, twenty amino acids are available for the formation of proteins. In this image, each amino acid present in the domain is represented by a particular colour: white, red, green, and light and dark blue, among others. The restlessness suggested by the image should be seen as a virtue, since proteins have to be flexible in order to function.

Este maremágnum de luces y colores corresponde a una porción o dominio de una proteína presente en todas las células del organismo. Se trata de una enzima del grupo de las cinasas, capaz de activar a otras proteínas. Su relación con la virología es tan sólo indirecta, pues al virólogo le interesa únicamente su estructura. Las cinasas, como todas las proteínas, están formadas por cadenas de aminoácidos. La naturaleza puede escoger entre 20 aminoácidos distintos, cada uno de ellos representados en la imagen por un color diferente: blanco, rojo, verde, azul celeste, azul marino, etcétera. La sensación de agitación que transmite la imagen es en realidad una cualidad, puesto que las proteínas deben ser flexibles para funcionar correctamente.

SH3 domain, part of the enzyme p56-lck-tyrosine kinase. Nuclear magnetic resonance spectroscopy, Werner Klaus, H. Hiroaki, Hans Senn, Roche Basel.

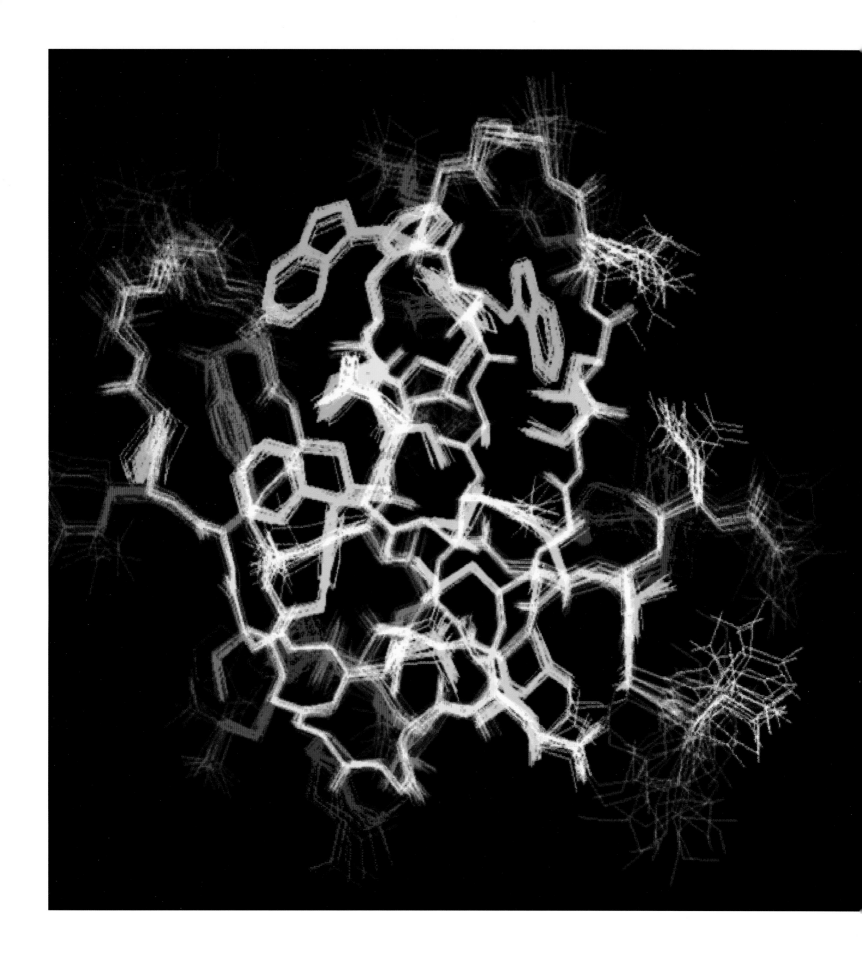

Viele gelbgefärbte Aids-Viren auf einer in kühlem Blau gehaltenen Zelloberfläche. Man wundert sich über die Unebenheit der Wirtszelle und staunt entweder über die Winzigkeit der Viren oder die Größe der Zelle, die hier nur zu ahnen ist. So gefährlich die Viren sind, das Bild erweckt den Eindruck, man könne die gelben Punkte einfach wegwischen, wenn man wollte. Just so, wie man sich Staubkörner aus den Augen wischt. Aber da gibt es einen entscheidenden Unterschied. Die Viren sind näher am Leben als der Staub. Deshalb gelingt es ihnen auch, sich stärker daran festzuklammern.

En jaune, des virus du sida campant à la surface d'une cellule colorée en bleu. Doit-on s'étonner davantage de la taille minuscule des virus ou de la grandeur de la cellule, dont on ne voit ici qu'une partie? On sait le danger que représentent ces virus qui, pourtant, donnent ici l'impression qu'on pourrait les balayer d'un simple geste. Comme on se frotterait les yeux pour en chasser les grains de poussière que le vent y a mis. A ceci près que les virus, plus proches de la vie que les grains de poussière, sont mieux armés pour s'y accrocher.

Here we see a large number of human immunodeficiency viruses that appear yellow on a cool blue cell surface. We are struck by the unevenness of the host cell and the minuteness of the viruses in relation to the cell, the size of which we can only guess at. In contrast to the very real danger posed by these viruses, the image creates the impression that we could simply wipe away the yellow spots, as we might brush away specks of dust that have blown into our eyes. But there is a crucial difference: unlike dust, viruses are closely related to living things and are designed to remain attached to them.

Multitud de virus del sida teñidos de amarillo sobre la superficie de un linfocito T teñido de azul. Llama la atención la rugosidad de la superficie celular, pero sobre todo el contraste entre las dimensiones diminutas de los virus y el enorme tamaño del linfocito, sólo visible en una pequeña parte. Los virus, es bien sabido, son peligrosísimos, pero en esta imagen da la impresión de que estos puntitos amarillos podrían eliminarse de un soplo, como motas de polvo que hubieran entrado en el ojo. Hay, no obstante, una diferencia esencial: que los virus están más cerca de la vida que el polvo y, por tanto, mejor dotados también para fijarse a la superficie celular.

Human immunodeficiency viruses budding out of a T-cell. Transmission electron microscopy, Charles Craig, Roche Welwyn.

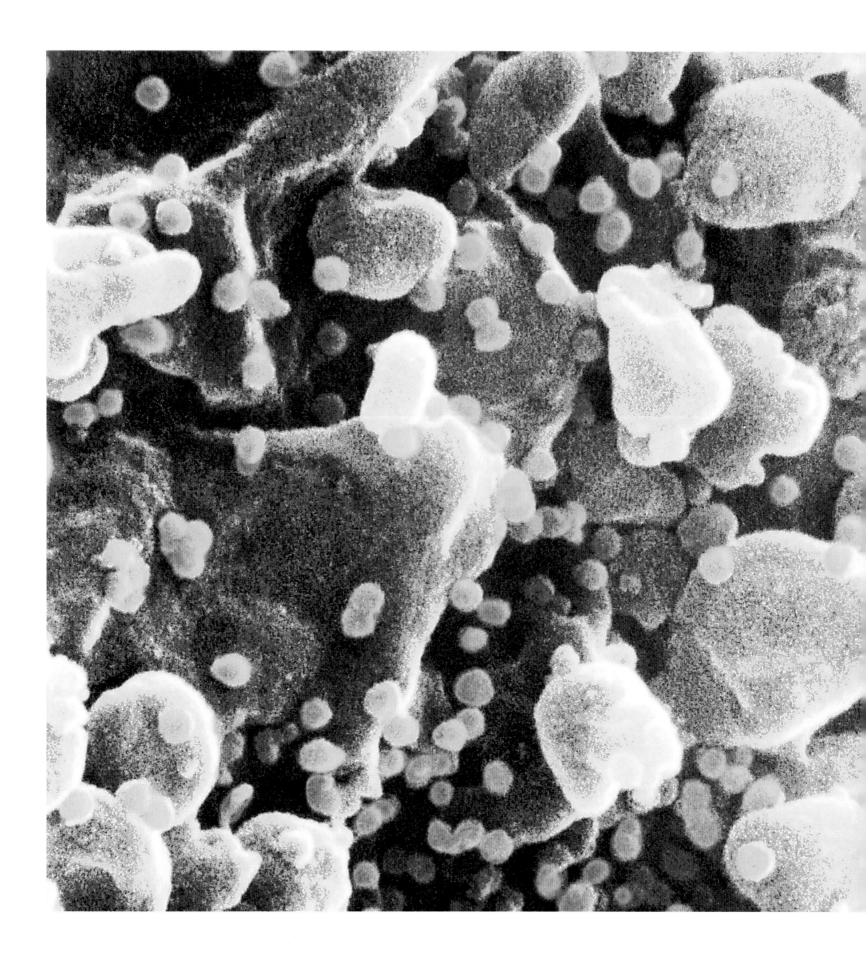

Viren können wirksam blockiert (inhibiert) werden, wenn es gelingt, ihre molekularen Werkzeuge auszuschalten. Solche Stoffe gibt es, und dieses Bild zeigt, was passiert, wenn einer Maus, die unter einer Leberentzündung (Hepatitis) leidet, ein so genannter Hepatitis-C-Protease-Inhibitor verabreicht wird. Nach kurzer Zeit verteilt sich die Markierung, die den Inhibitor anzeigt, über weite Strecken im Organismus, wobei die Farbe Rot die Stellen mit dem höchsten Wert kennzeichnet. Eine Ordnung ist dabei nicht leicht zu erkennen, was die Spannung für den Betrachter wie auch den Forscher erhöht.

Pour peu que l'on parvienne à rendre leurs outils moléculaires inopérants, il est possible d'inhiber ou de bloquer l'activité des virus. On voit ici ce qui se produit lorsqu'on administre à une souris atteinte d'hépatite un inhibiteur de la protéase de l'hépatite C, auquel on a pris le soin d'ajouter un marqueur. Peu de temps après l'administration, on retrouve ce dernier dans une grande partie de l'organisme, le rouge indiquant les endroits où la substance atteint les plus fortes concentrations. L'image titille d'autant plus l'imagination du chercheur qu'il est difficile de discerner un quelconque principe d'ordre.

Viruses can be effectively blocked (inhibited) by substances that switch off their molecular machinery. This image shows what happens when a radiolabelled hepatitis C protease inhibitor is administered to a mouse infected with hepatitis. Shortly after being administered, the radiolabelled substance is seen to be widely distributed in the body, the areas of highest concentration appearing as red. The lack of any obvious pattern heightens the tension both for the observer and for the scientist.

Los virus pueden inhibirse o bloquearse de forma eficaz con fármacos capaces de inutilizar sus mecanismos moleculares. En esta imagen podemos ver lo que ocurre cuando a un ratón con hepatitis se le administra un medicamento marcado que actúa inhibiendo la proteasa del virus de la hepatitis C. Al poco tiempo, el marcador aparece distribuido por gran parte del organismo, y el color rojo indica los lugares en los que se alcanzan mayores concentraciones del fármaco. No resulta fácil discernir ningún tipo de orden, lo cual supone un elemento de tensión tanto para el observador como para el investigador.

Distribution of a radiolabelled compound (antisense oligonucleotide) in a mouse; whole body autoradiography. Steve Harris, Roche Welwyn.

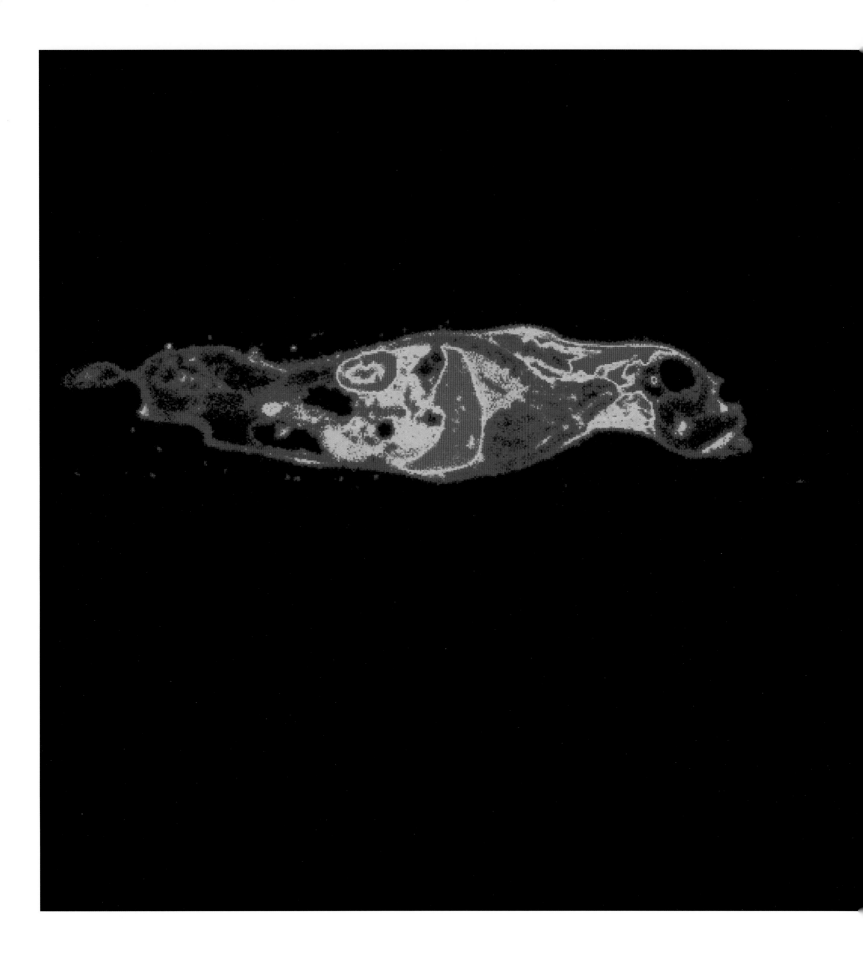

Die rote Kugel, die aus dem grünen Meer auftaucht, stellt ein Aids-Virus dar, das der Zelle des Immunsystems entschlüpft ist, mit deren Hilfe es sich vermehrt hat. Die rote Farbe erweckt Aufmerksamkeit und signalisiert die Gefahr, die sich hier zeigt. Wer im Übrigen die Oberfläche der Zelle und ihre vielfach gekrümmte und nirgendwo glatte Form betrachtet, kann sich nur wundern über die Sicherheit, mit der Viren hier eindringen und austreten können. Das Geheimnis ihres Erfolges muss tiefer liegen, als wir sehen können. Es muss in den Molekülen zu finden sein, denen sich die Forschung zuwendet, um die Präzision zu verstehen, mit der eine Virusinfektion vonstatten geht.

Cette sphère rouge émergeant d'un bouillonnement verdâtre est un virus du sida éclos de la cellule immunitaire dont il a besoin pour synthétiser ses propres constituants. Le rouge s'impose à l'attention et signale le danger que représente le virus. A regarder la surface de la cellule, tout en courbures et sans aucune partie lisse, on ne peut que s'étonner de la facilité avec laquelle les virus y pénètrent et en ressortent. Le mystère de cette facilité doit être plus profond que ce que l'œil permet de voir. Il doit se situer au niveau des molécules, que les chercheurs interrogent pour essayer de comprendre dans ses plus infimes détails le mécanisme d'infection.

The red sphere emerging from a green sea is a human immunodeficiency virus that has just detached itself from the immune cell in which it has replicated. The red colour attracts our attention and signals the danger seen in this image. It seems extraordinary that the virus is so easily able to penetrate and emerge from cells whose surface is so endlessly curved and irregular. The secret of the virus's success must lie at a deeper level – in the molecules to which scientists are now turning their attention in order to discover how viruses are able to infect cells with such a high degree of precision.

Esta esfera roja que emerge de un verde mar es un virus del sida que abandona el linfocito del que se ha servido para multiplicarse. El color rojo llama la atención y es señal de peligro. Observando la superficie celular del linfocito, con infinidad de recodos y nunca lisa, uno no puede dejar de admirarse ante la facilidad con la que los virus la atraviesan para entrar y salir de la célula. El secreto de ello debe de estar más profundamente de lo que los ojos nos permiten ver: en las moléculas que los científicos investigan para intentar comprender con precisión el mecanismo íntimo de la infección vírica.

HIV budding out of a T-cell. Transmission electron microscopy, Charles Craig, Roche Welwyn.

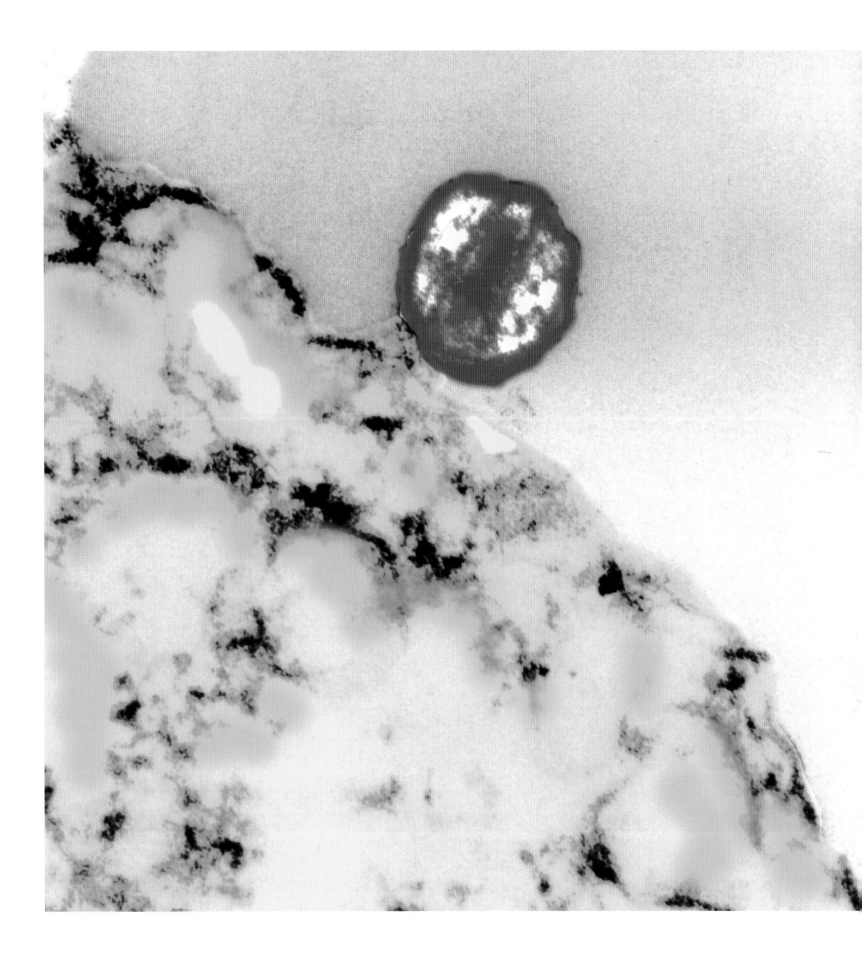

Die molekulare Struktur der Interferone kann auf verschiedene Weise dargestellt werden. In der hier gezeigten Abbildung eines Interferons, das als Medikament zur Behandlung von Hepatitis C eingesetzt wird, sind die spiralförmigen Anteile besonders hervorgehoben, die sich schraubenförmig winden. Die so genannte Alpha-Helix wurde zu Beginn der 1950er Jahre zum Vorbild für die Form der Doppelhelix, der Struktur des Erbmaterials. Die Schönheit der molekularen Schrauben würden die Griechen aus der Harmonie der Teile und deren Einfügung in das Ganze deuten. Unser Auge ist zum Glück dafür gemacht, diese Schönheit zu erfassen.

Il existe plusieurs façons de représenter la structure moléculaire des interférons. Celui que l'on voit ici est utilisé comme médicament dans le traitement de l'hépatite C. L'image insiste plus particulièrement sur les parties spiralées de la protéine, qui font penser à un pas de vis. Les scientifiques ont donné à cette structure le nom d'hélice alpha. Elle préfigurait, au début des années 1950, la structure en double hélice de l'ADN. De la beauté de ces spires moléculaires, à laquelle est heureusement sensible l'œil humain, les Grecs retiendraient sans doute l'harmonie des parties et l'élégance avec laquelle elles s'insèrent dans le tout.

The molecular structure of interferons can be represented in various ways. This image of an interferon that is used as a drug to treat hepatitis C highlights the corkscrew-like parts of the molecule. This protein structure, which is known as an alpha helix, is reminiscent of, but was discovered some time before, the double helix of DNA, our genetic material. The ancient Greeks would regard the beauty of the helical structure of these molecules as resulting from the harmony of the parts and their incorporation into a whole. Happily, our eyes are designed to appreciate this beauty.

La estructura molecular de los interferones puede representarse de muy diversas formas. En esta ocasión se trata de un interferón utilizado por los médicos en el tratamiento de la hepatitis C. Destacan en la imagen las partes espirales de la proteína, que recuerdan a un sacacorchos. Los científicos las llaman «hélices α», y sirvieron a mediados del siglo XX de prototipo para la estructura en doble hélice del ADN. Los antiguos griegos hubieran interpretado la belleza de estas espirales moleculares a través de la armonía de las partes y su integración en el todo. El ojo humano, por suerte, está especialmente diseñado para captar esta belleza.

Structure of the human protein interferon alfa-2a. Nuclear magnetic resonance spectroscopy, Werner Klaus, Bernard Gsell, Alexander M. Labhardt, Beat Wipf, Hans Senn, Roche Basel.

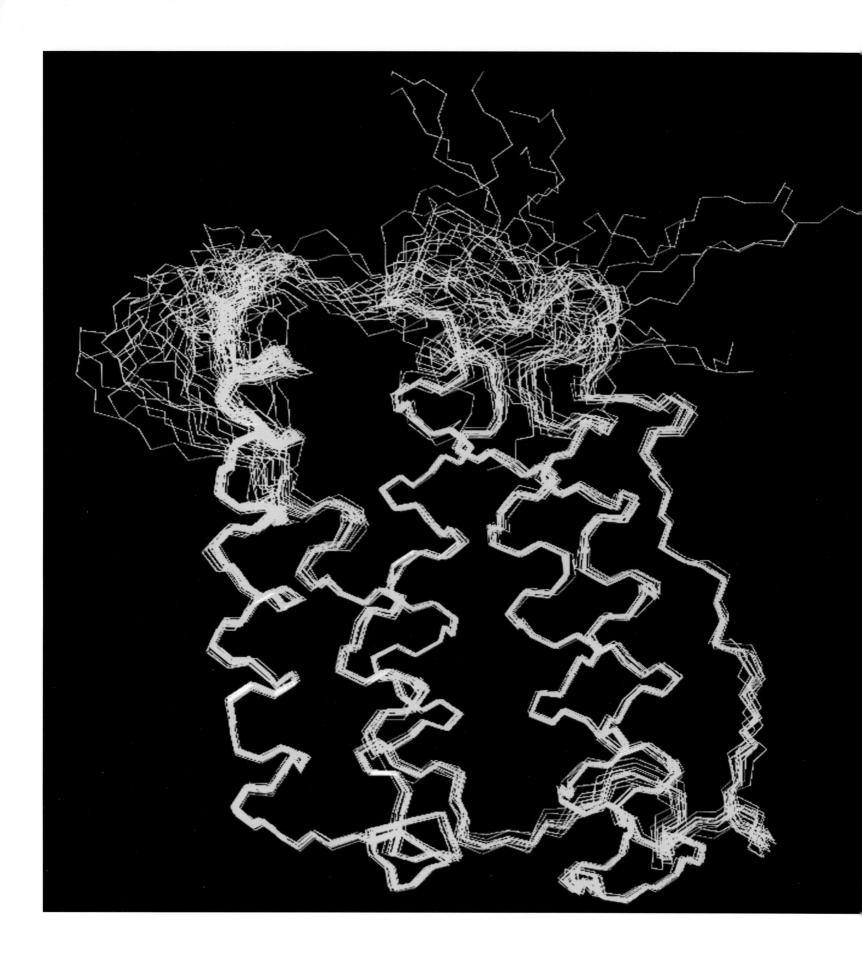

Herpes, so heißt das Virus, das wir hier in seiner ganzen Pracht sehen. Das weiße Zentrum gibt an, wo das genetische Material steckt, das wie das der Menschen aus DNA besteht. Der dunkelblaue Fleck unterscheidet sich vom roten Umriss der Hülle, in der das Virus steckt, durch die Schärfe seines Randes. Das Wort «Herpes» stammt übrigens aus dem Griechischen und heißt eigentlich «schleichender Schaden». Und es scheint, dass sich das Virus auf vielen Wegen anschleichen kann.

Le virus que l'on voit ici dans toute sa splendeur est le virus de l'herpès (herpèsvirus). Au centre de l'image, formant une tache blanche, son matériel génétique, constitué d'ADN, comme celui de l'homme. La tache bleue contraste nettement, grâce à sa bordure clairement dessinée, avec le rouge vif de l'enveloppe entourant le virus. Le mot herpès, qui vient du grec et signifie «mal rampant», rappelle que le virus a mille façons de ramper vers sa proie.

Herpes is the name of the virus shown here in all its splendour. The white centre is the site of the virus's genetic material, which, like that of humans, is composed of DNA. A sharply defined border separates the dark blue area from the red envelope that surrounds the virus. The word 'herpes' comes from the Greek herpein, meaning 'to creep' – just as this virus seems able to creep over many paths.

El virus que contemplamos aquí en todo su esplendor es el virus del herpes. El centro blanco indica la localización de su material genético, formado, exactamente igual que el nuestro, por ADN. La zona azul oscura se distingue claramente de la llamativa cubierta roja que envuelve al virus. La palabra «herpes» procede del verbo griego herpein, que significa «arrastrarse», y le cuadra bien, desde luego, a este virus de aspecto rastrero, que parece avanzar arrastrándose.

Herpes virus. Transmission electron microscopy, Charles Craig, Roche Welwyn.

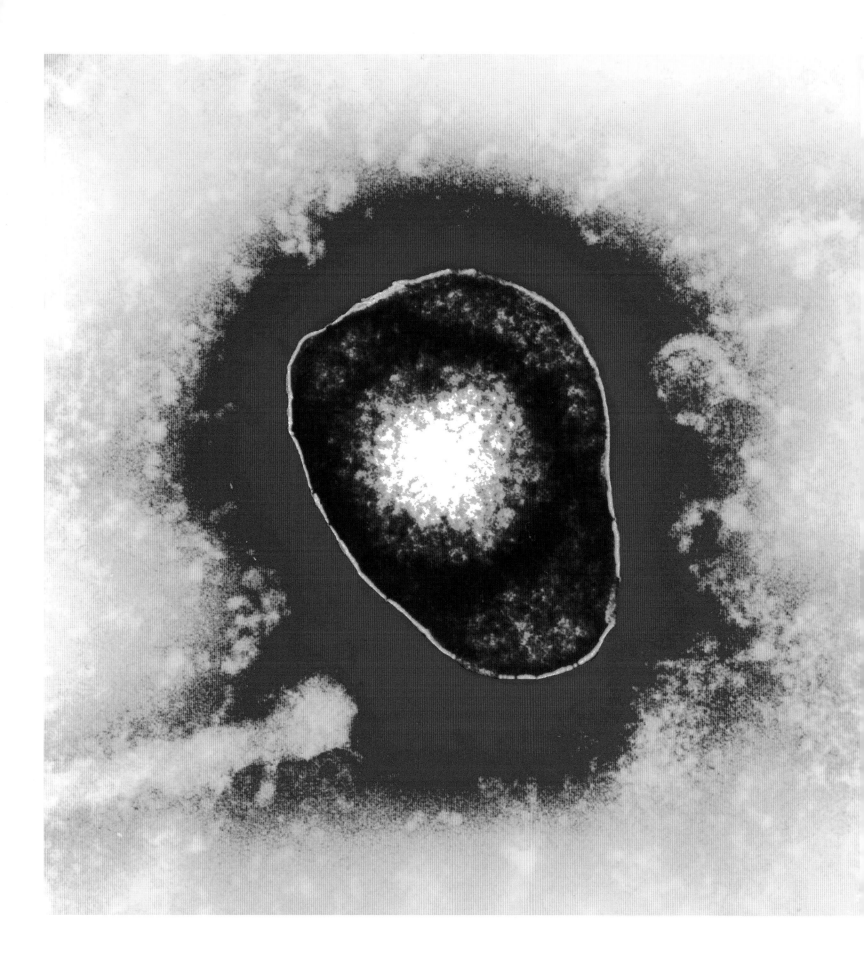

Es ist nie nur ein Aids-Virus, das seiner Wirtszelle entschlüpft. Es sind immer sehr viele, die austreten und sich weiter ausbreiten. In einem Fall meint man, den Ablösevorgang des Virus von der Zelle direkt mitverfolgen zu können, und es scheint sogar, als ob er mit aller Schnelligkeit und auf ein bestimmtes Ziel hin vollzogen würde. Doch Viren sind nichts als Moleküle, und sie haben kein Ziel, selbst wenn dies noch so naheliegend zu sein scheint. Das Ziel der Forscher, die die Viren untersuchen, ist dagegen klar gesteckt. Es besteht darin, die Viren genau an dem zu hindern, was sich zwar auf dem Bild in aller Ruhe betrachten lässt, was aber viele Menschen in Unruhe versetzt.

C'est toujours en grand nombre que les virus du sida éclosent de la cellule hôte et se répandent dans l'organisme. On croirait, pour l'un d'entre eux, être témoin de l'instant précis où il se détache de la cellule. On a même l'impression que cela se fait très vite et dans un but bien déterminé. Mais les virus ne sont jamais que des molécules, auxquelles il est impensable, quelles que soient les apparences, de prêter un projet aussi élaboré. Les chercheurs qui les étudient, en revanche, agissent dans un but bien précis: les empêcher de faire ce qu'on leur voit faire ici en toute impunité et qui est si dangereux pour l'homme.

When a human immunodeficiency virus emerges from a host cell to spread and infect new cells, it is always just one of many. In some cases it seems that the process by which the virus detaches itself from a cell can be followed in detail, and it may even seem that the process takes place at great speed and with a specific goal in mind. But, as plausible as such an explanation of their behaviour may seem, viruses are no more than molecules, and they have no goals. By contrast, scientists who study viruses have a very clear goal in mind, namely to prevent the viruses from harming large numbers of people via the process that we are fortunate enough to be able to observe in complete safety in this image.

Cuando los virus del sida abandonan su célula hospedadora para diseminarse por el organismo, lo hacen siempre en gran número, y nunca un solo virus por célula. Para un virus concreto, no obstante, uno puede tener la sensación de presenciar el momento concreto en que se desprende de la célula, e incluso la impresión de que lo hace rápidamente y con una finalidad bien precisa. Los virus, sin embargo, no son más que moléculas y, por engañosas que sean las apariencias, carecen de un objetivo determinado y elaborado. Quienes sí lo tienen, y bien definido, son los virólogos: impedir precisamente que los virus lleven a cabo lo que vemos en la imagen, que puede tener consecuencias mortales para el ser humano.

HIV budding out of a T-cell. Transmission electron microscopy, Charles Craig, Roche Welwyn.

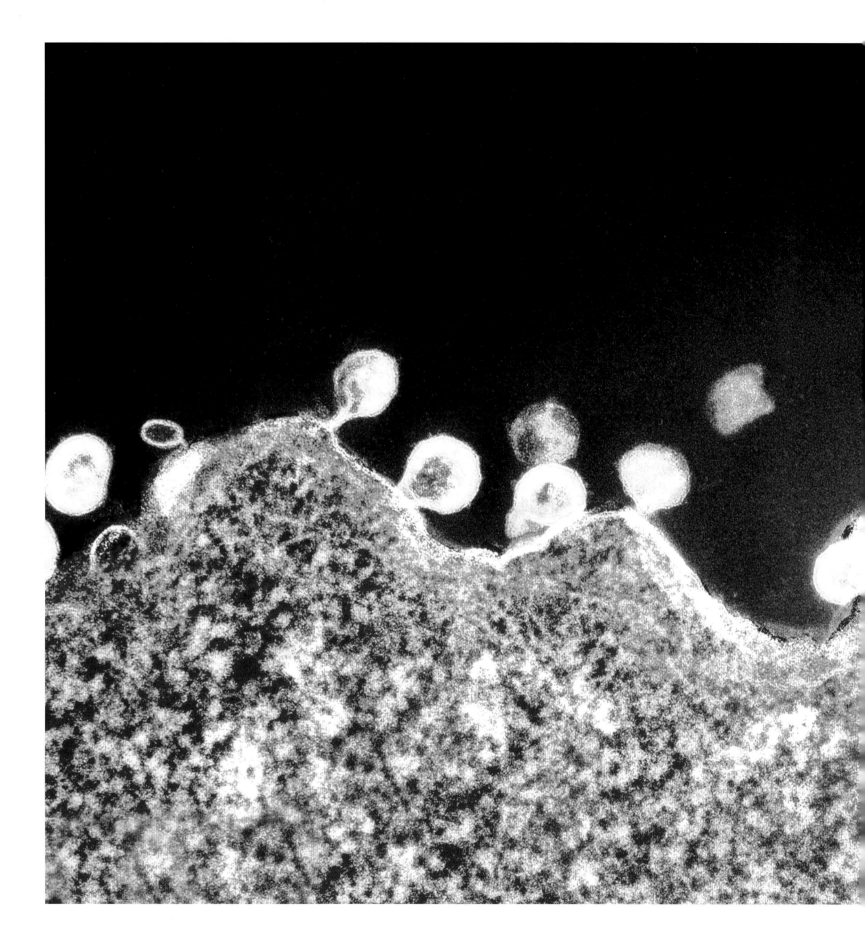

Onkologie

Herausforderung

L'oncologie

Le défi

Oncology

Challenge

Oncología

Reto

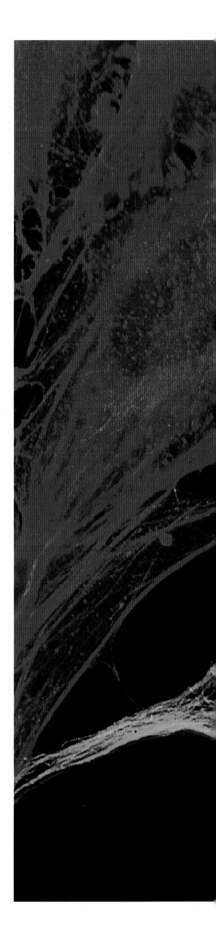

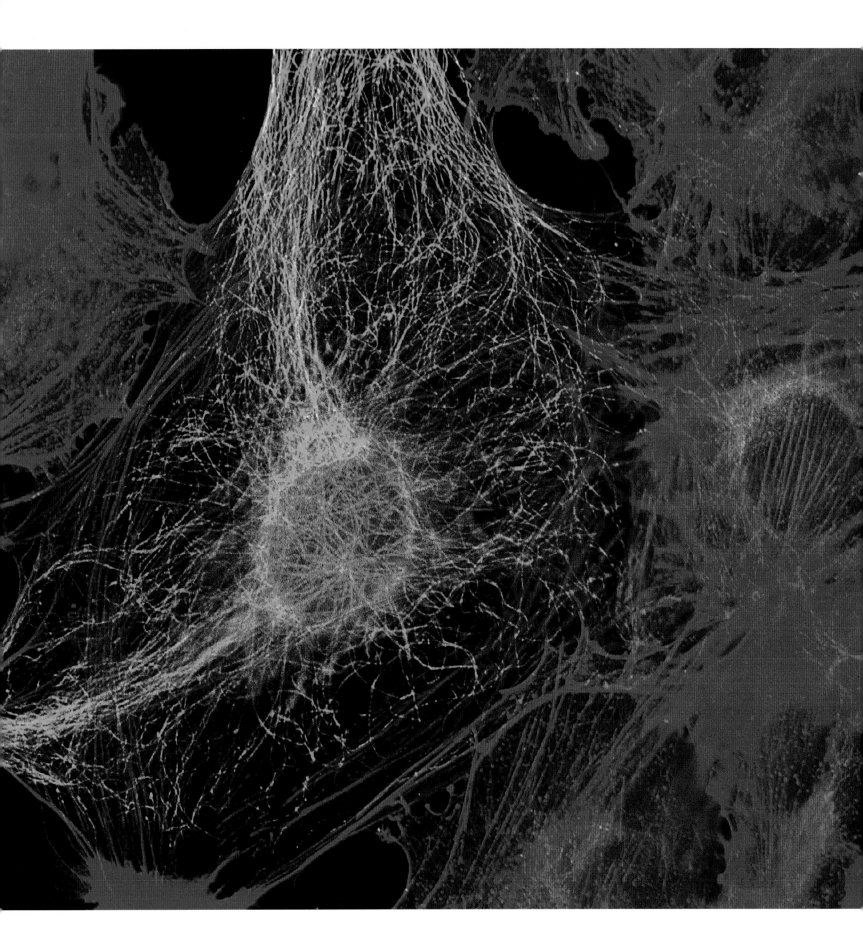

Herausforderung

Le défi

Krebs ist ein Wort, hinter dem sich sehr viele – zu viele – Krankheiten verbergen. So groß das Spektrum der verschiedenartigen Zellen auch ist, die krebsförmig entarten und dem Leben um sie herum Einhalt gebieten können, die Anstrengungen der Forschung müssen größer sein, um sie im Zaum zu halten. Sie schlägt dazu verschiedene Wege ein. Wenn heute von Krebsforschung die Rede ist, dann tragen dazu Genetiker ebenso bei wie Zellbiologen, Immunologen und Biochemiker, um nur ein paar Disziplinen zu nennen. Im Zentrum der Aufmerksamkeit stehen die Zellen selbst, die sich eine neue Form geben und so das Krebsgewebe bilden, das keinen Stillstand kennt und immer weiter wächst und wuchert. Von außen gesehen ist die Form einer Zelle – und damit ein ästhetisch begreifbares Kriterium – entscheidend für ihre Gefährlichkeit und unsere Gefährdung. So wird verständlich, warum es die Morphologen – die kundigen Kenner der Gestalt – sind, die sich ihnen mit besonderer Aufmerksamkeit widmen. Das Studium der Zellen dient natürlich weitgehend sachlichen Zielen und diagnostischen Zwecken, aber völlig kann sich auch der Wissenschaftler der Schönheit dieser Bilder nicht entziehen. Er erlebt, was Künstlern ein selbstverständlicher Gedanke ist, dass nämlich oft dort, wo Schönheit wahrgenommen wird, der Schrecken nicht lange ausbleibt.

Le cancer est un nom générique désignant de très nombreuses maladies. Si grand que soit le spectre des cellules pouvant se cancériser et détruire la vie autour d'elles, la recherche doit faire, pour les en empêcher, des efforts plus grands encore. Elle a, pour cela, le choix entre plusieurs voies. La recherche sur le cancer est aujourd'hui un domaine où interviennent aussi bien des généticiens que des spécialistes de la biologie cellulaire et de l'immunologie ou des biochimistes, pour ne citer que quelques-unes des disciplines concernées. L'intérêt des chercheurs se porte essentiellement sur les cellules qui, en changeant de forme, constituent le tissu cancéreux, lequel s'étend alors et prolifère sans ne plus connaître de cesse. Vue du dehors, la forme de la cellule – critère esthétiquement appréhensible – est un indicateur déterminant de sa dangerosité, et l'on comprend donc que les morphologistes, c'est-à-dire les spécialistes de l'étude des formes, s'y intéressent autant. Si ce n'est pas pour leur beauté mais pour des raisons scientifiques qu'ils étudient les cellules, les chercheurs ne peuvent toutefois rester insensibles au spectacle qu'ils découvrent sous le microscope. Ils éprouvent, en le contemplant, une sensation bien connue des artistes, qui savent que la beauté annonce souvent l'horreur.

PP. 134/135: Osteosarcoma cell in cell culture. Fluorescence microscopy, Olaf Mundigl, Roche Penzberg.

Challenge

Reto

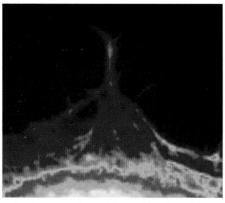

The word 'cancer' can be applied to a great many – sadly, too many – diseases. The sheer variety of cells that can undergo malignant degeneration and thereby bring life in their vicinity to a standstill underlines the scale of the problem faced by scientists in their efforts to halt the proliferation of malignant cells. In order to achieve this, they have to explore many different paths. Cancer research involves contributions by geneticists, cell biologists, immunologists and biochemists, among other specialists. At the centre of attention are the actual cells that undergo malignant transformation to form tissue that grows and proliferates without respite. As it is the external form of a cell that provides our senses with a concrete indication of the danger posed by that cell, it is morphologists – experts on the form and structure of living things – who devote themselves to the study of cancer cells. Of course, cells are studied largely for practical reasons, including their potential for use as diagnostic aids, but even scientists cannot fail to be moved by the beauty of the images of cells shown here. When viewing these images, scientists perceive something that many artists feel to be self-evident, namely, that where there is beauty, terror is often not far away.

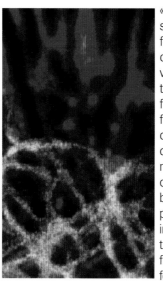

«Cáncer» es un término genérico que se aplica a muchas –demasiadas– enfermedades. La variedad de células capaces de malignizarse y destruir la vida en torno a sí es muy grande, y tanto o más grandes aún son los esfuerzos de los científicos por poner freno a la proliferación de las células cancerosas. La investigación sobre el cáncer es hoy una labor multidisciplinaria en la que intervienen biólogos celulares, inmunólogos, genéticos y bioquímicos, junto a muchos otros especialistas. En el centro mismo de la investigación se hallan las células transformadas que se multiplican sin fin y forman el tejido canceroso. La forma externa de una célula –que es un criterio estético perceptible por los sentidos– resulta indicativa de su peligrosidad, de modo que es comprensible el interés de los morfólogos (especialistas en la forma y la estructura de las células) por las células cancerosas. Los científicos estudian las células por motivos científicos y diagnósticos, pero difícilmente pueden permanecer impasibles ante la belleza de las imágenes que el microscopio les ofrece. Contemplándolas, los científicos experimentan una sensación que para los artistas resulta evidente: que allí donde hay belleza suele ocultarse a menudo el espanto.

Rot-Gelb-Grün – drei Farben, die eng im Spektrum nebeneinander liegen und hier benutzt worden sind, um drei der insgesamt 23 Chromosomen-Paare anzufärben, die zu einer menschlichen Zelle gehören. Es ist offensichtlich, dass eine genaue wissenschaftliche Analyse zahlreiche Feinstrukturen beschreiben könnte – etwa die Mittelpunkte der rot gefärbten Strukturen oder die Unterschiede in der Farbdichte zwischen dem kürzeren und dem längeren Ende der gelb erscheinenden Chromosomen. Aber wir können uns auch nur auf das Farbenspiel konzentrieren. Allein der ästhetische Eindruck vermittelt, was man zwar weiss, aber oft vergisst, dass nämlich die Chromosomen in Paaren zusammengehören und sich gegenseitig ergänzen.

Rouge, jaune, vert. Trois couleurs très proches les unes des autres dans le spectre, utilisées ici pour colorer trois des 23 paires de chromosomes de la cellule humaine. Une analyse approfondie permettrait évidemment au spécialiste de différencier toute une série de structures fines: par exemple, les taches jaunes visibles sur les structures colorées en rouge ou les différences de densité de couleur entre le bras long et le bras court des chromosomes apparaissant en jaune. Mais on peut également se contenter de jouir du spectacle qu'offrent les couleurs, qui nous rappellent un fait connu, mais souvent oublié, à savoir que les chromosomes vont par paires complémentaires les unes des autres.

Red, yellow and green, three colours that lie close to each other in the spectrum, have been used here to 'paint' three of the 23 chromosome pairs present in human cells. Clearly, a scientific examination of this image could identify a wealth of detail, such as the centres of the red structures or the differences in depth of colour between the shorter and the longer arms of the yellow chromosomes. Alternatively, we could simply consider the interplay of colours, the aesthetic aspect of the image. This alone suffices to tell us something that we already know, but can easily forget, namely that chromosomes come in complementary pairs.

Rojo, amarillo y verde: tres colores vecinos en el espectro cromático, y utilizados aquí para colorear tres de los 23 pares de cromosomas que contienen las células humanas. El análisis científico detallado de esta imagen permite al especialista, por supuesto, apreciar multitud de detalles, como el punto amarillo central de los cromosomas pintados en rojo o las diferencias de densidad cromática entre los brazos cortos y los brazos largos de los cromosomas amarillos. Pero podemos concentrarnos también exclusivamente en la impresión estética del juego de colores, suficiente para recordarnos algo sabido, pero que con frecuencia olvidamos: la disposición de los cromosomas en pares complementarios.

Chromosome painting of human metaphase chromosome spread. Fluorescence microscopy, Max Planck Institute for Biochemistry, Martinsried.

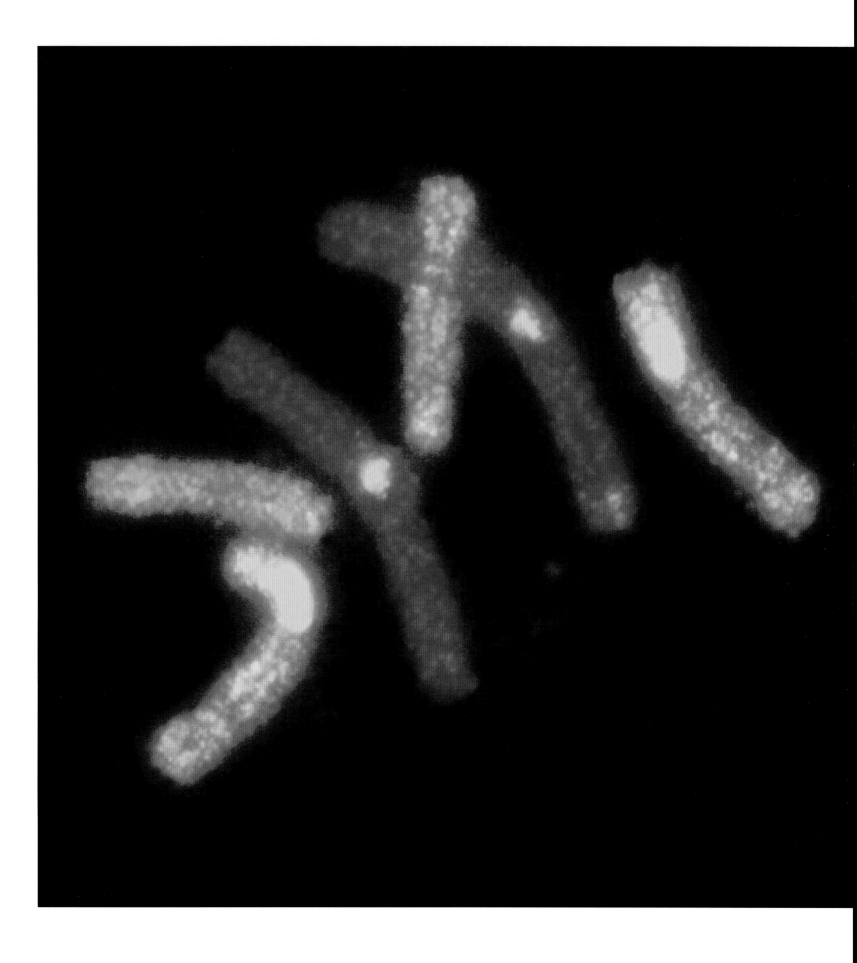

Bildungszelle des Bindegewebes – so definiert das Lexikon den Fachausdruck für die Fibroblasten, deren prächtiges Innenleben hier gezeigt wird. Die mit fluoreszierenden Farbstoffen und immunbiologischer Hilfe markierte Zelle zeigt ein reichhaltiges und farbenprächtiges Innenleben mit einem in Pink gehaltenen Kern und den in Grün aufleuchtenden Molekülen, die den Zellraum aufspannen. Die Farbe Rot zeigt dasselbe an wie im Alltag, nämlich Gefahr. An den so erkennbaren Positionen sitzt der gesuchte Rezeptor. Das therapeutische Ziel ist also gefunden, und nun gilt es, Nutzen aus dem Schönen zu ziehen.

Cellule jeune, précurseur du tissu conjonctif, telle est la définition que le dictionnaire donne des fibroblastes, dont on a ici un magnifique aperçu. Réalisée à l'aide de colorants fluorescents et de techniques immunobiologiques, cette image montre une cellule où domine un splendide noyau rose, entouré de molécules vertes. Le rouge est, comme toujours, un signal de danger, et c'est sur les sites apparaissant en rouge que loge le récepteur auquel s'intéresse ici le chercheur. Voilà donc trouvée la cible médicamenteuse. Reste, maintenant, à tirer du beau un parti thérapeutiquement utile.

Cells that form connective tissue is the dictionary definition of fibroblasts, such as the one whose vibrant inner life is seen here. This cell has been immunologically labelled and stained with fluorescent dyes to reveal an abundant and colourful inner life, with a pink nucleus and a rim of green molecules surrounding the cell body. The colour red signifies the same as it does in everyday life: danger. Here it shows the positions of a specific receptor that is to be used as a target of therapy. Now that this receptor has been found, the challenge facing scientists is to derive some benefit from this beauty.

Célula precursora del tejido conjuntivo; así definen los diccionarios especializados el tecnicismo «fibroblasto», cuyo aspecto puede apreciarse en esta magnífica fotografía obtenida mediante técnicas de inmunomarcado y tinción con colorantes fluorescentes. En el interior de esta fibroblasto multicolor se distingue claramente el núcleo rosado y diversas moléculas citoplásmicas de color verde. El color rojo indica, como de costumbre, una señal de aviso; en este caso, la presencia de un receptor que podría servir como diana molecular para nuevos medicamentos. La belleza puede también ser provechosa.

NIH3T3 fibroblast overexpressing the EGF receptor in culture. Fluorescence microscopy, Olaf Mundigl, Roche Penzberg.

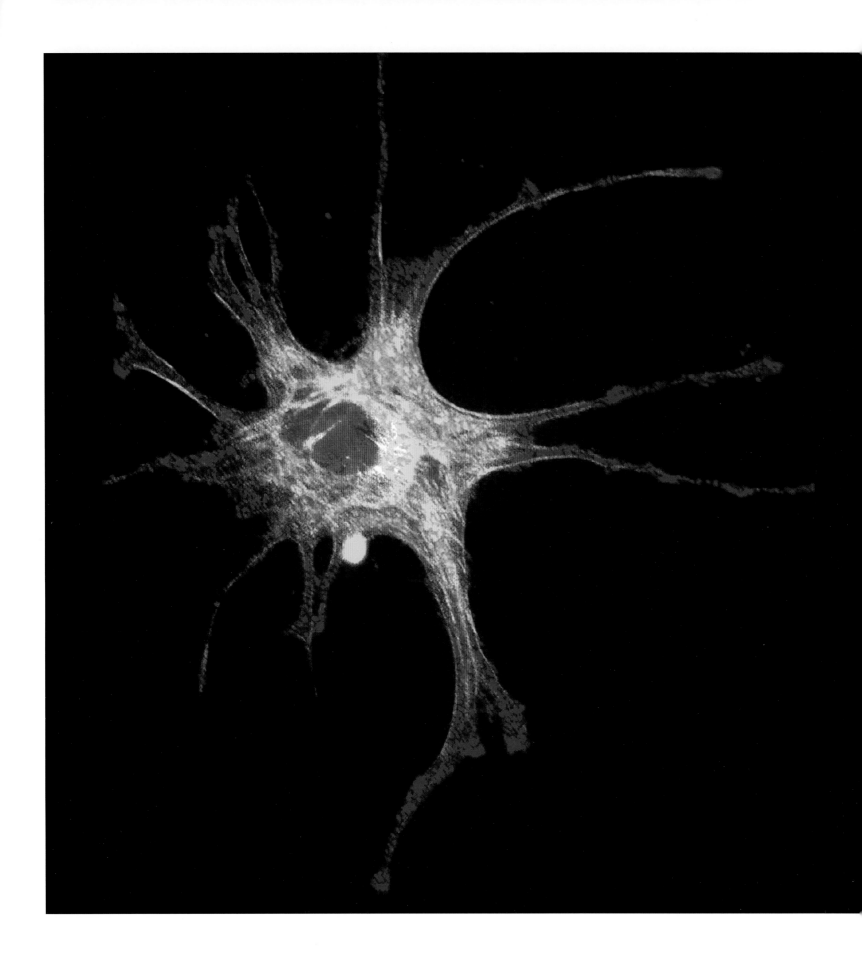

Charakteristisch für die Struktur des Kleinhirns (Cerebellum) sind die nach dem Physiologen Jan Purkinje benannten Zellen. Als Wissenschaftler hat Purkinje ein Phänomen beschrieben, das Künstlern längst vertraut war, nämlich der Umschlag der Wahrnehmung, wenn das Licht sich ändert. Auf dem Bild sehen wir einen Schnitt mit vielen Purkinje-Zellen, deren rote Färbung verrät, dass sie zahlreiche Rezeptoren für Wachstumsfaktoren auf ihrer Oberfläche tragen. Mit ihnen reguliert eine Zelle ihr Wachstum, und von ihnen kann man lernen, warum dessen Kontrolle leider zu oft misslingt und Krebs die Folge ist. Der blaue Untergrund zeigt die Zellkörper, in dem auch die gelb-grünen Spuren der Ausläufer zu erkennen sind, die in die nächste Schicht des Kleinhirns hineinreichen. Mit ihm versucht unser Körper, seine Balance zu halten.

On appelle cellules de Purkinje, du nom d'un physiologiste tchèque, les volumineux neurones de l'écorce grise du cervelet. Purkinje a notamment décrit les modifications de la sensibilité de la vision dues aux changements de la lumière, phénomène que connaissent bien les artistes. Les cellules de Purkinje que l'on voit sur cette coupe apparaissent en rouge, signe de la présence à leur surface de nombreux récepteurs de facteurs de croissance. La cellule utilise ces facteurs pour réguler sa croissance. Quand cette dernière n'est pas convenablement contrôlée, ce qui est très souvent le cas, se développe un cancer. En bleu, les corps des cellules, en vert et jaune leurs prolongements, qui poussent leurs ramifications jusque dans la couche suivante du cervelet. Le cervelet est la structure du cerveau qui contrôle l'équilibre.

Purkinje cells are a characteristic structural feature of the cerebellum. The physiologist Jan Purkinje, after whom these cells were named, described a phenomenon with which artists had long been familiar, namely the change in perception that occurs with changes in light. In this image, we see a section through many Purkinje cells, the red colour of which betrays the fact that their surface bears many receptors for growth factors. By studying these growth factors, we can learn why the control of cell growth all too often fails, giving rise to cancer. The blue in the lower part of the image indicates the cell bodies. In these we can make out yellow-green traces of the cell extensions that reach up into the next layer of the cerebellum. Among other things, this part of the brain helps us to keep our balance.

Las células de Purkinje son el elemento más característico de la corteza del cerebelo. El fisiólogo checo Jan Purkinje, de quien tomaron el nombre, describió además un fenómeno bien conocido por los artistas: las modificaciones de la percepción visual con los cambios de luz. En la imagen vemos un corte microscópico con muchas células de Purkinje teñidas de rojo, signo de que en su superficie portan numerosos receptores para los factores que regulan el crecimiento celular. Cuando esta regulación se altera, se origina el cáncer. El fondo azul corresponde a los cuerpos celulares, y los trazos verde amarillentos, a las prolongaciones dirigidas hacia la siguiente capa del cerebelo. El cerebelo es la estructura encefálica encargada de mantener el equilibrio.

Purkinje cells of the cerebellum from a frozen section of rat brain. Fluorescence microscopy, Olaf Mundigl, Roche Penzberg.

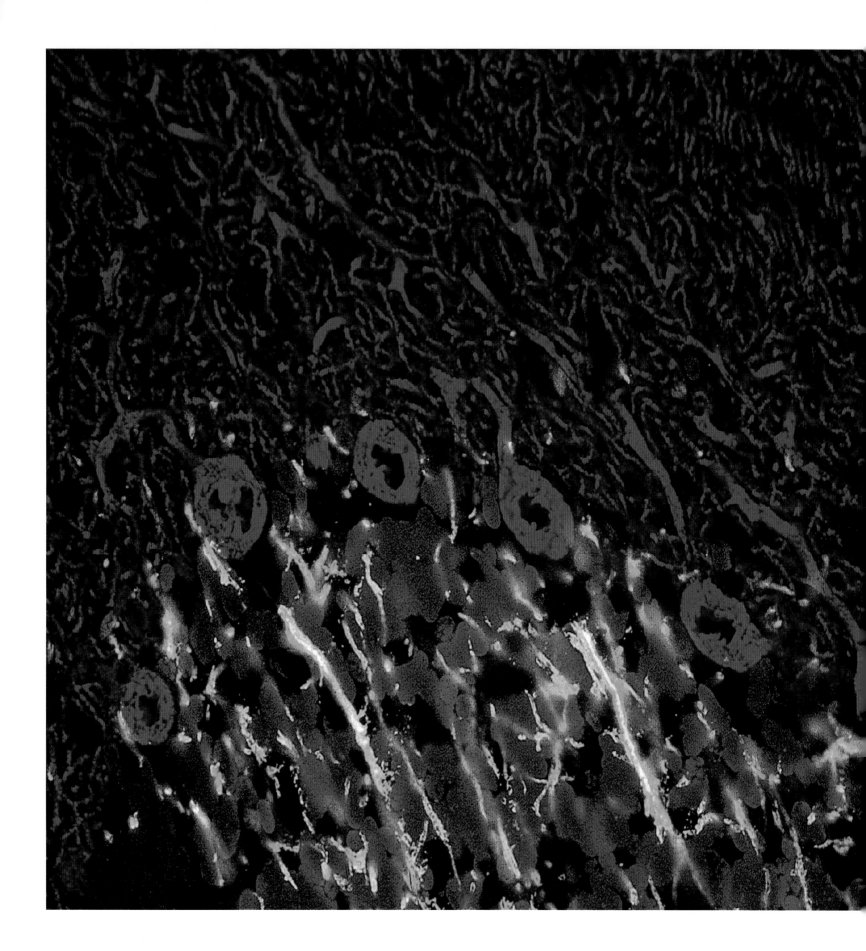

Zwei Krebszellen, die kurz vor ihrer Trennung stehen. Die rot-gelbe Farbe markiert die Moleküle, die für die zelluläre Dynamik sorgen. Sie tun alles, um die Trennung zu ermöglichen, und zeigen zugleich, wie genau eine Zelle regulieren kann, was an welcher Stelle in ihrem Innenraum geschieht. Die Farben zeigen dem Betrachter, wie hochgradig organisiert die Einheit des Lebens ist, die selbst viele Untereinheiten erkennen lässt, und zwar sowohl hinsichtlich der Struktur – sichtbar in den Chromosomen – als auch hinsichtlich der Funktion – erkennbar an dem glühenden Fleck im Zentrum, der die scheinbar ruhig abwartenden Bereiche um ihn herum trennt und unabhängig macht.

Deux cellules cancéreuses sur le point de se diviser. Le rouge et le jaune correspondent aux molécules qui entretiennent la dynamique cellulaire. Faisant tout pour faciliter la division, elles donnent en même temps une idée de la précision avec laquelle les cellules parviennent à réguler leurs processus internes. Les couleurs témoignent du haut degré d'organisation de l'unité de la vie, dont on distingue sur l'image les nombreuses sous-unités, les unes structurelles, les autres fonctionnelles, reconnaissables à la tache incandescente, tout au centre de l'image, où vont se séparer, et prendre leur indépendance, les éléments qui, apparemment, attendent tranquillement cet instant.

Here, we see two newly formed cancer cells shortly before their final separation. Red and yellow indicate the molecules that bring about the separation of the cells. This is a fine example of the precision with which cells regulate their inner life. The colours show how cells, the basic units of life, are divided into many sub-units with respect both to structure – as seen in the chromosomes – and to function – as seen from the intense red spot in the centre, which is in the process of separating the areas around it into two independent entities.

Dos células cancerosas a punto de dividirse. El rojo y el amarillo corresponden a las moléculas que intervienen en la separación celular. Constituyen una buena muestra de la precisión con que las células regulan los procesos de su vida interior. Los colores ponen de manifiesto el elevado grado de organización de las células, unidades básicas de la vida, formadas a su vez por multitud de subunidades, tanto estructurales como funcionales, reconocibles en la mancha incandescente central donde habrán de separarse las demás zonas celulares que parecen aguardar tranquilas ese crítico momento.

Mitosis of human cervical carcinoma cells. Fluorescence microscopy, Olaf Mundigl, Roche Penzberg.

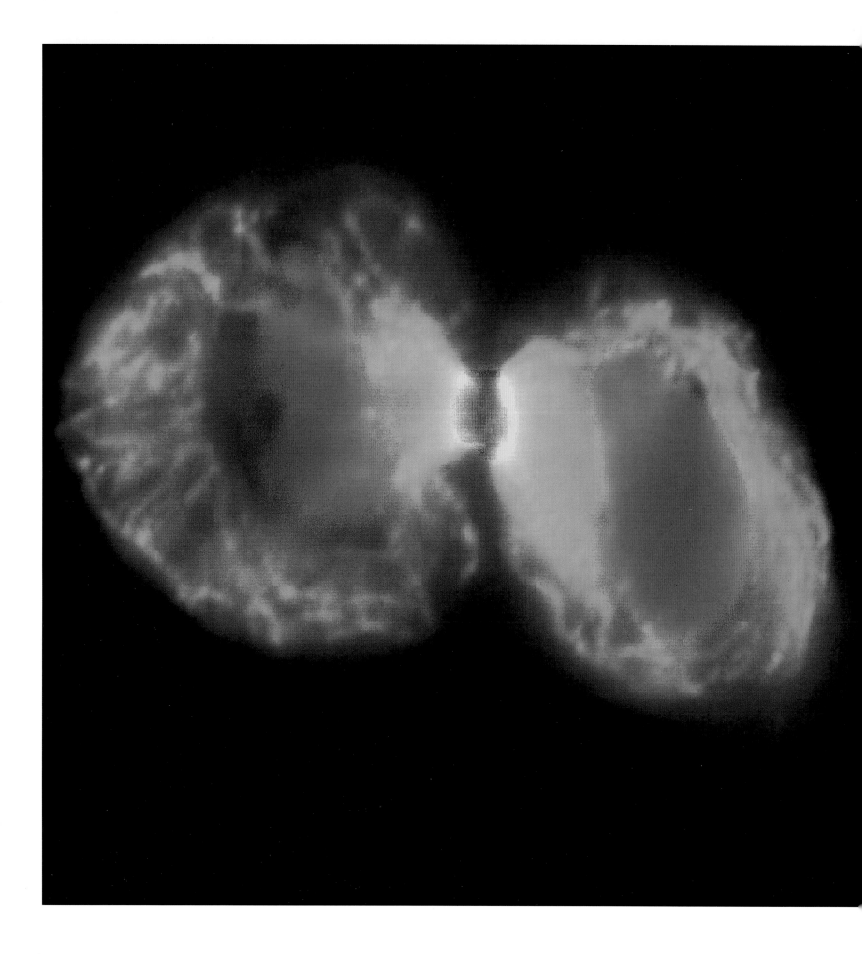

Was hier wie ein Halsreif aussieht, entpuppt sich im Blick der Wissenschaft als die Schleife, durch die es den Zellausläufern gelingt, zu dem grünen Wachstumskegel zurückzukehren, dem sie entwachsen sind. Lange Ausläufer dieser Art bringen nur Nervenzellen zustande, und sie verlieren diese Fähigkeit nicht, wenn sie aus der natürlichen Umgebung genommen und in die Kulturschale gebracht werden. Gelungen ist die Aufnahme mit einem Fluoreszenzmikroskop, mit dessen Hilfe die Wissenschaftler vor allem nach Faktoren suchen, die das Wachsen entarten und gefährlich werden lassen.

Ce qui apparaît ici comme un tour de cou est en réalité la boucle que décrivent les prolongements cellulaires pour réintégrer le cône de croissance dont ils sont issus. Seules les cellules nerveuses développent d'aussi longs prolongements, ce qu'elles font également lorsqu'elles sont élevées en culture. Cette image a été réalisée à l'aide d'un microscope à fluorescence, instrument dont les scientifiques se servent surtout pour étudier des facteurs capables de dérégler et de rendre dangereux les mécanismes de croissance de la cellule.

The necklace-like structure seen here is in fact the loop through which extensions of a neuron return to the green growth cone from which they have arisen. Only nerve cells develop extensions of this length, and they retain the ability to do so even when removed from their natural environment and placed in a culture dish. This image was produced using a fluorescence microscope, an instrument that scientists have found to be particularly useful in the search for factors that cause disordered and dangerous growth of cells.

Esto que parece un collar es en realidad el asa que describen las prolongaciones de una neurona para regresar a su cono de crecimiento original, en verde. Sólo las neuronas son capaces, incluso cuando se cultivan en el laboratorio, de desarrollar prolongaciones tan largas. Esta imagen se obtuvo con un microscopio de fluorescencia, muy utilizado por los científicos para investigar los factores que pueden alterar la regulación del crecimiento celular.

Growth cone of an immature hippocampal neuron developing in vitro. Fluorescence microscopy, Olaf Mundigl, Roche Penzberg.

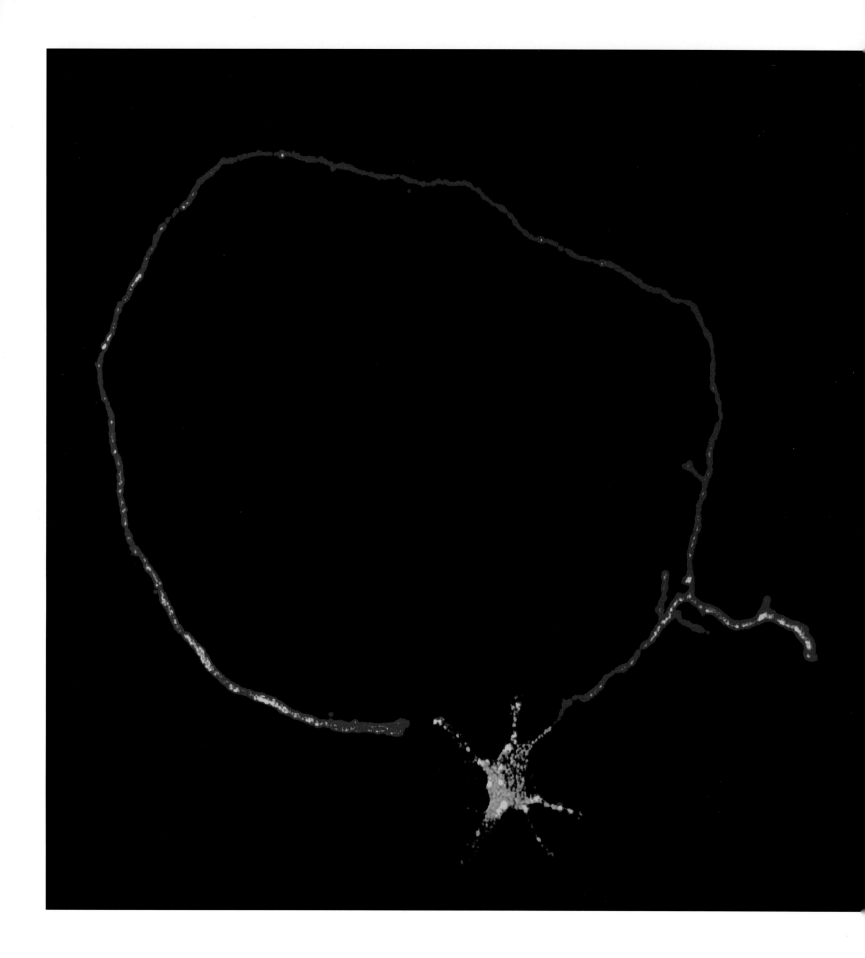

Wenn Krebszellen in Lösungen gehalten werden, nehmen sie oft eine runde Form an. Es scheint, als ob sie dabei die innen sichtbare – blaugrün gefärbte – Gestalt des Kerns übernehmen. Dies passiert nicht, wenn sie wie hier auf einer Fläche zu liegen kommen. Der gelbrote Kranz der Brustkrebszelle, der den Kreis des Kerns auflöst, markiert die Orte, an denen sich das molekulare Instrumentarium der Zelle befindet, das ein unkontrolliertes Vermehren verhindern soll.

Conservées dans une solution, les cellules cancéreuses prennent souvent une forme arrondie, comme pour adopter celle du noyau, que l'on distingue, coloré en bleu vert, à l'intérieur de cette cellule provenant d'une tumeur du sein. Ce phénomène ne se produit pas lorsque les cellules reposent, comme ici, sur une surface plane. La couronne jaune rouge, qui dissout le rond du noyau, indique les endroits de la cellule où se trouvent les instruments moléculaires censés l'empêcher de proliférer de manière incontrôlée.

When suspended in solution, cancer cells often take on a rounded shape like that of their nucleus, stained blue-green in this image. This does not occur when, as here, they are placed on a surface. In this image of a breast cancer cell, the yellow-red ring seen within the nucleus indicates the location of the molecular machinery of the cell that normally serves to prevent uncontrolled cell growth.

En una disolución, las células cancerosas adoptan a menudo una forma redondeada semejante a la de su núcleo, de color azul verdoso en esta imagen. No ocurre así cuando, como es aquí el caso, la célula reposa sobre una superficie plana. La corona rojiamarilla visible en el núcleo de esta célula de cáncer de mama marca la localización de los instrumentos moleculares que impiden a la célula multiplicarse de forma incontrolada.

Breast tumour cell with internalised model antagonist for p53/mdm2 binding. Fluorescence microscopy, Olaf Mundigl, Roche Penzberg.

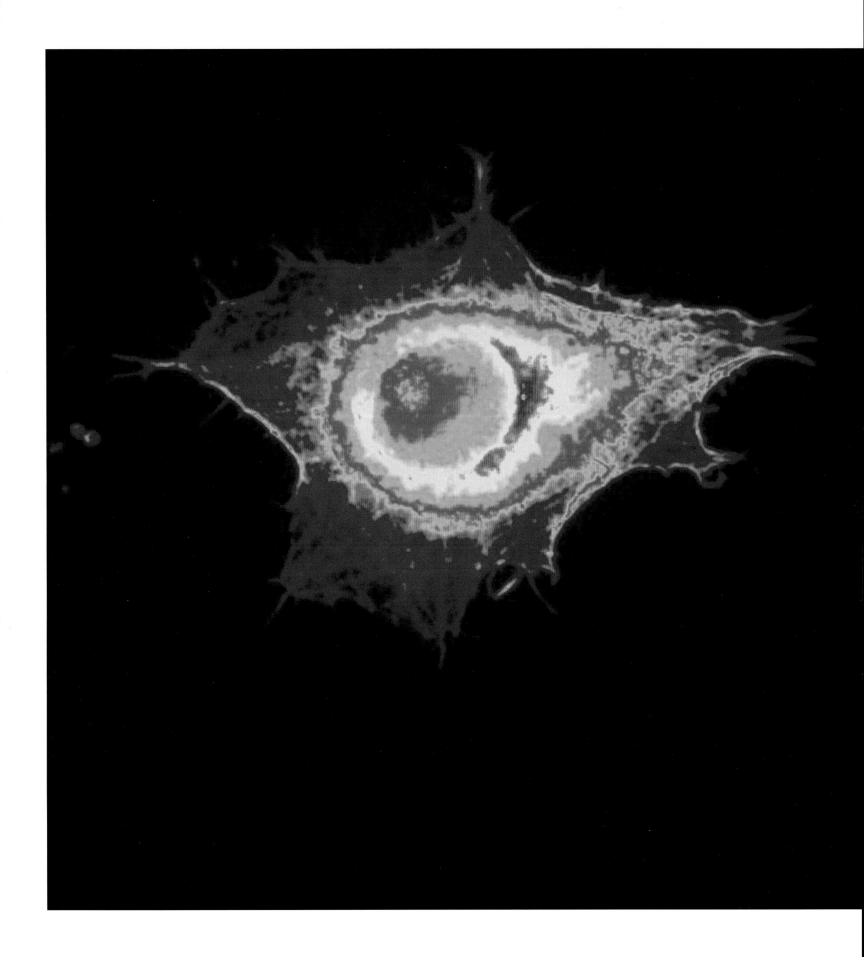

Bevor Wissenschaftler die Genese (Entstehung) von Tumorzellen verstehen können, müssen sie ein geeignetes Modell finden, an dem die grundlegenden Vorgänge der Krebsentstehung studiert werden können. Eine Möglichkeit liefern die Zellen des Nervensystems, die sich in Kulturschalen züchten lassen. Man sieht die grünen Ausläufer eines solchen Neurons, die dicht und drängend mit roten und gelben Punkten besetzt sind. Sie zeigen die Stellen an, die dazu dienen, Kontakt mit anderen Zellen aufzunehmen. Man spricht dabei von Synapsen und weiß, dass der Kontakt zwischen den Zellen nicht direkt erfolgt. Es bleibt ein Zwischenraum. Daher erscheinen die bunten Punkte wie hingetupft.

Pour comprendre la genèse des cellules cancéreuses, les scientifiques doivent d'abord concevoir des modèles leur permettant d'étudier les mécanismes de base de la cancérisation. Ici, des cellules du système nerveux élevées en culture. En vert, les prolongements du neurone. Les points rouges et jaunes, très serrés, qui en occupent la surface marquent l'emplacement des synapses, autrement dit des régions de contact entre deux neurones. Ce contact n'est jamais direct. Il reste toujours, entre les deux, un espace où se répand le médiateur chimique de la transmission de l'influx nerveux. C'est l'existence de cet espace qui fait que les points apparaissent comme de simples touches de couleur, posées de la pointe du pinceau.

In order to understand how tumour cells arise, scientists require a suitable model in which the basic processes of cancer formation (carcinogenesis) can be studied. One such model is provided by the cells of the nervous system, which can be grown in culture dishes. The green extensions of the neuron seen here are studded with red and yellow spots. These represent sites at which the cell can make contact with other cells. At these 'synapses', contact between the cells is not direct, but via a gap. The brightly coloured spots therefore have the appearance of having been dabbed on.

Para conocer el origen del cáncer, los científicos necesitan un modelo biológico adecuado en el que poder estudiar los mecanismos carcinogénicos básicos. Uno de tales modelos lo constituyen los citocultivos neuronales. Las verdes prolongaciones de esta neurona muestran en su superficie infinidad de puntitos rojos y amarillos, que corresponden a las sinapsis o puntos de contacto entre dos neuronas. El contacto entre dos neuronas no es nunca directo, sino que deja entre ambas un espacio intersináptico. Y es precisamente la existencia de dicho espacio lo que explica que los puntos coloreados parezcan como aplicados con la punta de un pincel.

Hippocampal neuron in cell culture. Fluorescence microscopy, Olaf Mundigl, Roche Penzberg.

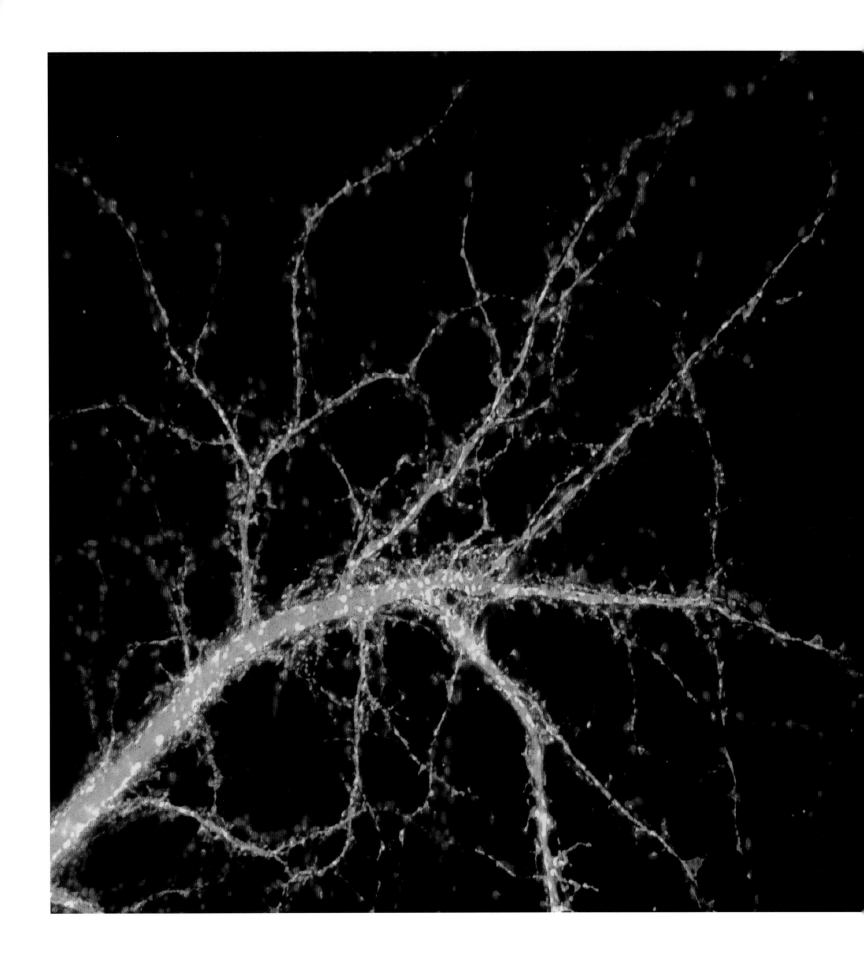

Im Mittelpunkt vieler Bemühungen zum Verständnis von Krebskrankheiten steht schon seit langem der Brustkrebs. Wenn Zellen aus einem entsprechenden Tumor als einzelne Schicht kultiviert werden, entstehen Bilder wie dieses hier. An dessen abstrakten Formen erstaunt, wie viel Platz die dunkelblauen Zellkerne benötigen, die von roten Filamenten umrahmt werden. Die entscheidende Farbe auf dem Bild ist Grün. Sie deutet das Vorhandensein eines Proteins an, dem es gelingt, die Tumorbildung zu unterdrücken. Warum fehlt es zwischendurch? Warum gelingt dies nicht immer?

Le cancer du sein est depuis longtemps un objet d'études privilégié pour les chercheurs qui s'efforcent de mieux comprendre les mécanismes généraux du cancer. Voici l'image que peuvent offrir les cellules d'une tumeur du sein lorsqu'on les élève en culture, de manière à obtenir une monocouche comme celle que l'on peut voir ici. En bleu foncé, encadrés de filaments rouges, les noyaux cellulaires, qu'on est frappé de voir tenir autant de place. La couleur la plus intéressante de l'image n'est pourtant ni le bleu foncé ni le rouge, mais le vert, qui signale la présence d'une protéine capable d'inhiber la formation de la tumeur. Pourquoi n'est-elle pas partout présente? Pourquoi son action inhibitrice est-elle parfois défaillante?

Breast cancer has long been a focus of efforts to understand malignant disease. When cells from a suitable tumour are cultivated in a single layer (monolayer), a pattern of growth such as that seen here can arise. A striking feature of the abstract forms seen in this image is the amount of space occupied by the dark blue cell nuclei, which are surrounded by red filaments. The key colour in this image is green. It indicates the presence of a protein that inhibits tumour formation. Why is this sometimes missing? Why does this defence mechanism sometimes fail?

El cáncer de mama es desde hace tiempo uno de los objetivos centrales de los esfuerzos científicos para comprender mejor los mecanismos patogénicos del cáncer. Cultivando las células cancerosas en una sola capa –o «monocapa»– se obtienen imágenes como ésta. En el maremágnum de formas abstractas llama la atención la gran cantidad de espacio que ocupan los núcleos celulares, de azul oscuro, rodeados de filamentos rojos. Para los científicos, no obstante, el color decisivo de esta imagen no es el rojo ni el azul, sino el verde, que indica la presencia de una proteína capaz de inhibir la formación del tumor. ¿Por qué no siempre está presente? ¿Por qué falla en ocasiones este mecanismo defensivo?

Breast tumour cells forming an epithelial cell monolayer in culture. Fluorescence microscopy, Olaf Mundigl, Roche Penzberg.

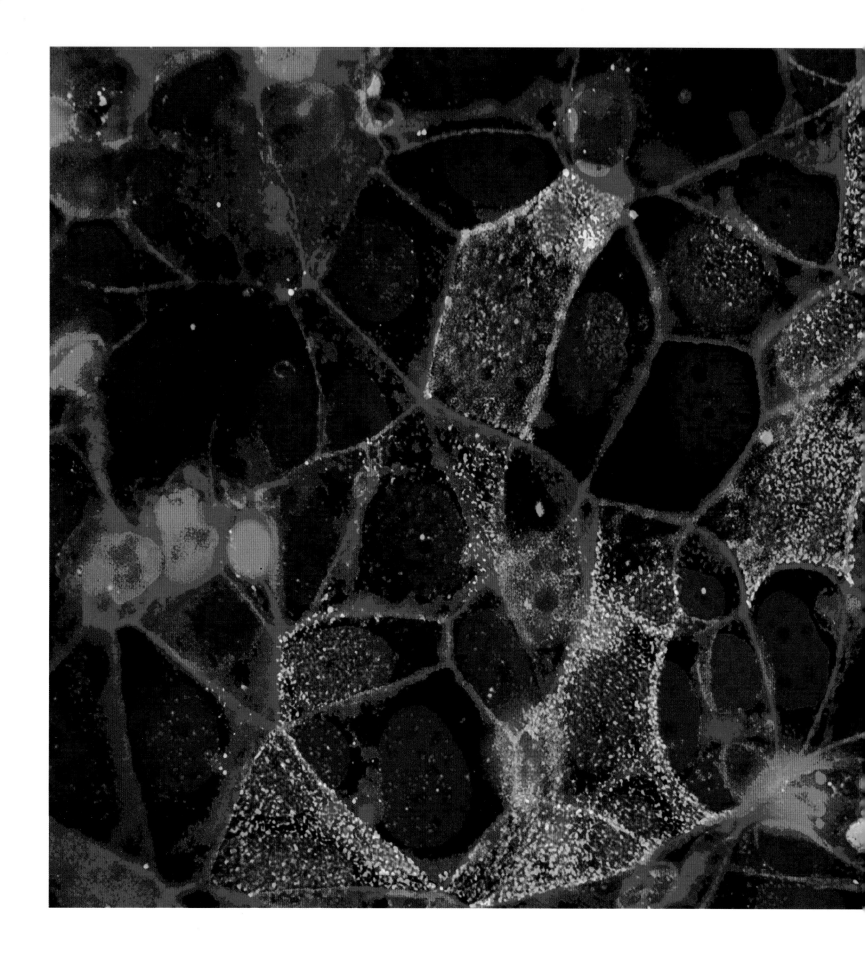

Technisch gesehen handelt es sich bei dieser Darstellung um Zellen, die aus Insekten stammen und ein Übermaß eines bestimmten Proteins herstellen. Auch für den Betrachter, dem diese Details nicht präsent sind, wird in der sichtbaren Außenbewegung der Zelle die Überproduktion augenfällig – als ob etwas nach außen drängte, ohne ein Ziel zu haben, das erreicht werden könnte. Wir kennen viele Strukturen aus dem Alltag, die so ähnlich aussehen, und darin liegt sicher auch der Grund, warum wir meinen, auf etwas Vertrautes zu blicken. Man glaubt zu verstehen, warum die großen Wissenschaftler und Künstler der Renaissance Analogien zwischen dem Mikrokosmos und dem Makrokosmos herstellten. So konnten sie verstehen, und wir können es ihnen nachtun.

Provenant d'insectes, les cellules que l'on voit ici présentent la particularité de fabriquer des quantités excessives d'une certaine protéine. Même l'œil non exercé reconnaît un mouvement qui pousse vers l'extérieur, sans avoir de but précis. Nous vivons entourés de structures ressemblant à celle-ci et c'est sans doute ce qui lui donne cet air de déjà vu. A voir cette image, on comprend l'habitude qu'avaient les grands savants et les grands artistes de la Renaissance d'établir des analogies entre le microcosme et le macrocosme. C'était pour eux une clé du savoir. Nous avons, nous, le microscope.

In technical terms, this is an image of insect cells that are producing an excessive amount of a certain protein. However, even the untrained observer is struck by the impression of movement at the cell surface. It seems that something is trying to force its way outward, without heading for any particular destination. The fact that many structures from everyday life look like this undoubtedly explains why this image seems familiar. We feel we understand why the great scientists and artists of the Renaissance drew analogies between the microcosm and the macrocosm. It helped them – as it can help us – to achieve understanding.

Estas células, obtenidas de insectos, son capaces de sintetizar cantidades excesivas de cierta proteína. Incluso el observador ocasional percibe una impresión de movimiento en la superficie celular, como algo que tratara de salir sin un objetivo preciso. A la vista de esta imagen que nos resulta tan familiar, probablemente porque vivimos rodeados de estructuras semejantes a ella, uno entiende la costumbre que tenían los grandes científicos y artistas del Renacimiento de establecer analogías entre el microcosmos y el macrocosmos. Era para ellos –y puede seguir siéndolo para nosotros– una ayuda para alcanzar el saber.

Insect cells (SF9 cells) overexpressing GFP. Fluorescence microscopy, Olaf Mundigl, Roche Penzberg.

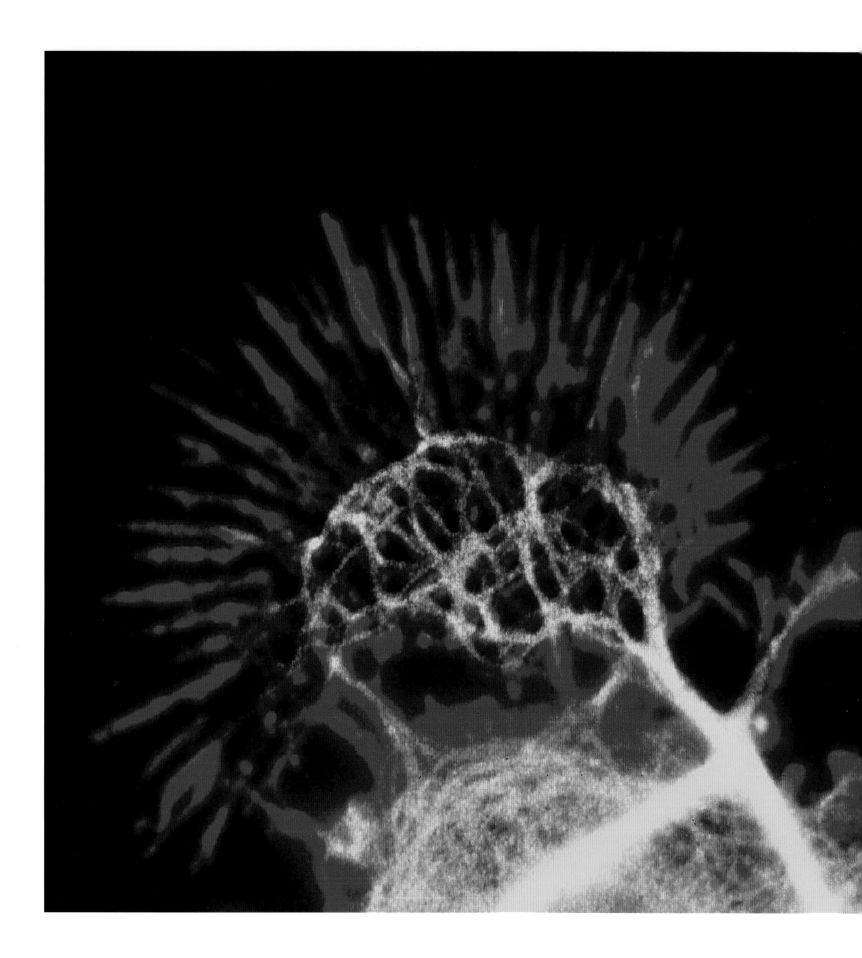

Onkologie
L'oncologie
Oncology
Oncología

Was im Auge des Betrachters wie ein hübsches Lichterspiel wirkt, signalisiert in der biologischen Wirklichkeit höchste Gefahr. Die gelben und roten Punkte auf den geschlossenen blauen Flächen markieren die Orte von Genen, deren Variation Krebs – Brustkrebs in diesem Fall – nach sich ziehen kann. Die bunten Punkte sind Abschnitte von Chromosomen, die stets als Paare in den Zellen vorliegen. Je mehr Farben die Wissenschaftler verwenden, desto spezifischer wird die Diagnose.

Le jeu de lumières, si agréable à l'œil, que l'on découvre ici est en réalité un signal biologique on ne peut plus alarmant. Les points jaunes et rouges qui se détachent sur les structures bleues clairement délimitées sont des sites génétiques dont la mutation peut provoquer un cancer, dans le cas particulier un cancer du sein. Ces points sont des segments de chromosomes, dont on sait qu'ils forment toujours des paires. Plus le scientifique utilise de couleurs différentes, plus le diagnostic est spécifique.

As pretty as they may be in this image, these sparkling lights are in fact a sign of extreme biological danger. The yellow and red spots seen on the rounded blue areas indicate the sites of genes which, by mutating, can give rise to cancer – in this case, breast cancer. The brightly coloured spots are segments of chromosomes, which always occur in pairs. The more colours are used in this technique, the more specific is the diagnosis.

Este hermoso juego de luces constituye en realidad una señal biológica de máximo peligro. Los puntos amarillos y rojos visibles en las estructuras azules marcan la localización de los genes cuyas mutaciones pueden provocar cáncer (en este caso, más concretamente un cáncer de mama). Estos puntos de colores corresponden a segmentos cromosómicos, dispuestos siempre por parejas. Cuantos más colores se utilicen en esta técnica, más específico será el diagnóstico.

Breast imprint. Fluorescence microscopy, Max Planck Institute for Biochemistry, Martinsried.

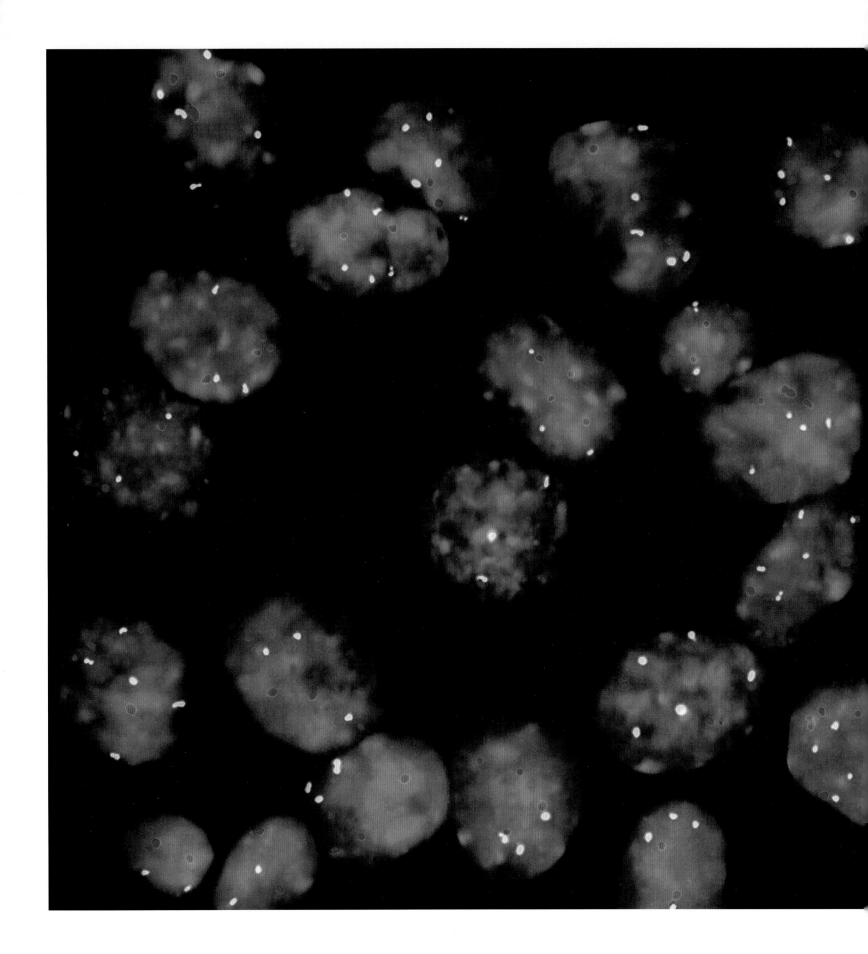

Quotations

P. 60   Natural science does not simply
         describe and explain nature;
         it is part of the interplay between
         nature and ourselves.

         Werner Heisenberg (1901 – 1976)

P. 74   Nothing is in the intellect
         that was not first in the senses.

         *St. Thomas Aquinas
         (1225 – 1274)*

P. 94   The technical view finds
         the secret of beauty
         in the complete correspondence
         of function and form.

         Adolf Portmann (1897 – 1982)

P. 110   Everything in the world ist strange
         and marvellous to well-open eyes.

         *José Ortega y Gasset
         (1883 – 1955)*

P. 134   In art as in science, the essential is
         to experiment. ... Most of the time,
         such experiments lead to nothing.
         Occasionally, however, the most
         extravagant experiment suddenly
         opens up a new path.

         *François Jacob (*1920)*

Concept and design	Beat Schenk
Reproductions	Lithoteam AG, Allschwil
Printers	Werner Druck AG, Basel
Binding	Grollimund AG, Reinach

7000488

© 2001, Editiones Roche

F. Hoffmann-La Roche Ltd
CH-4070 Basel

ISBN 3-907770-86-2